## Art and literature in the Groove

## Volume One Number One

All copyrights belong to the individual authors and artists.

## Thrilling
## Tales
Chicago, IL

www.ThrillingTales.com
www.Litbop.com

cover painting "Girls' Brunch" by Katherine Ace

book and cover designer—Tim Chapman
proofreader—Randall Jon Van Vynckt

# Contents

**Lit**bop

# *Contents*

## Art

## Photographs

## Cartoons

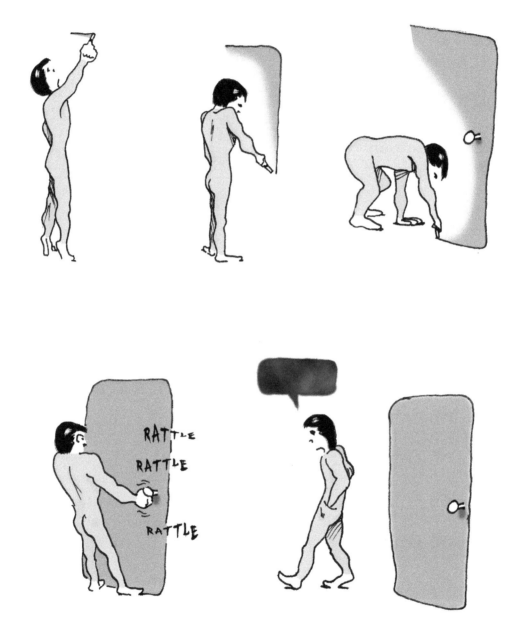

## *Editors Note*

Several months ago I submitted a story to a journal that advertised for previously published stories. This is a rare occurrence in publishing. Most editors refuse to look at work that's appeared elsewhere. A ten-year-old blog, a now-defunct magazine—it makes no difference; if it's been published before, it's editorial poison. The journal's editor was interested, but I wasn't willing to accept the story changes he wanted me to make. They would have shifted the focus away from my protagonist to a couple of secondary characters, so I withdrew my submission.

That experience got me thinking. *I bet other writers have stories that are itching for a new audience, too.* I sent out a request for submissions and got back some brilliant fiction and poetry. But I'm a visual person. I've spent long hours shambling through art museums and pouring over image-filled magazines and comic books (Make Mine Marvel). So I sent another request for

submissions to some talented artists and photographers. Voila! Litbop!

Why Litbop? Jazz (bebop in particular) is known for looking at music from unusual perspectives and for solo improvisations by one or more of the performers. Musical improvisation is the art of spontaneous composition, but musicians can't successfully compose music on the fly without having spent years studying theory and practicing chords and scales. In fact, bebop is so intricate an art form that musicians have invented dedicated scales for it. From jazz legends like Charlie Parker and John Coltrane to current players like Caroline Davis, jazz musicians have honed their skills to make their complex playing seem effortless. Likewise, the writers, artists, and photographers in Litbop have put in the work, and they've got the chops. I hope you'll enjoy their unique perspectives on life and art.

*photo by D. Kosiba*

Tim Chapman ○ Chicago ○ 2021

L. C. Fiore

## *IN LIMBO*

Jerry's got his panties in a wad because when we woke this morning we found on the new pallet the same porcelain and Fabergé curios we've been selling now for the better part of a week. This particular merchandise is a pain to set up and that's God's honest: each hand-painted women's shoe, each glittering, crystal rose, every stenciled teacup comes individually packaged in bubble wrap, so it's not only a matter of opening the shipping cartons and setting the contents out on counter displays—as we do for books or sporting equipment—but a tedious process of slicing open the cartons, removing each stowed item, unpeeling the Scotch tape with our bleeding fingernail nubs until we unfurl about a thousand yards of bubble wrap. Set-up takes forever for about a thousand delicate pieces.

"It's just not fair," Jerry says. "What did I do to deserve this?"

I break down empty boxes and toss them into the aisle for Service to pick up later. Asking myself the same question: What, indeed? What did I do to wind up not where a true believer might call Heaven, because this is no one's definition of paradise, but to also not find myself in Hell? Or that's what others who've been here much longer than me swear, that there's someplace worse.

Jerry curses trying to make the display endcap stand upright. A decade of this and still he can't quite figure out how it goes together. The display stand has about fifty wire arms sticking out. Inevitably, one comes loose as soon as he manages to get another one secured. From these we'll eventually hang porcelain figurines—moose and yodelers and milk cows—that bounce up and down on springs.

"Who the hell buys something like this?" Jerry wants to know. "Where the hell do they put these kinds of things?"

"Where in Limbo?" I smile wryly. "Where in *Purgatorio*?"

But the humor is lost on Jerry, here, where we sleep on hard cots each night in our booth. And when we wake, there's a new shrink-wrapped pallet of merch waiting: unpasteurized goat cheese, DVD players—whatever the cartons hold, it's always a surprise. A week straight selling the same precious knickknacks is starting to wear on us both.

At the register, I turn the key and the change drawer shoots open. It's stuffed with bills and coins I don't recognize, in denominations larger than what I knew as part of the Living. In the drawer are pale-blue bills that say 1000, and on the back is a picture of some barbarian king. The coins are familiar enough, silver and copper, and in friendly denominations: 1, 5, 10, 50. This is something else that changes daily. We never know what currency we'll be using until I—and it's always me now—open the cash drawer.

"What've we got?" Jerry dangles figurines from his fingertips like some giant, menacing puppeteer. The figurines grin and flex on their springs in long, aping loops.

"Forints," I tell him, "that's what…200 is about equal to a dollar?"

"Never heard of it."

Jerry won't touch the cash drawer since the time we were selling medieval armor and got stuck using ancient Chinese cowry shells. Around midday, Jerry realized he'd been making change in bone thinking it was wood, and so our end-of-day was way off. More than a grand. For a week after, we were stuck selling some pretty sick shit, Freak-Museum commodities like severed hands and blood worms and pig fetuses in jars of formaldehyde. The higher-ups weren't happy with our register being so far off, and that was a harsh punishment. The shrunken heads gave us nightmares for weeks.

This place, in what a practicing Catholic—as opposed to a *recovering* Catholic like me—might call Perdition, is built upon rewards and punishments. Mess up like we did with the cowry shells, the drawer gets off, and we're stuck selling earmuffs woven with human hair. Sell out our booth each day for a week, a month, a year, and who knows? Maybe we get upgraded.

"No one gets upgraded," Jerry has said many times. "People only go one direction. Down."

By *down* he means the Fiery Furnace, the Underworld—Hell. This is pretty good incentive for us to move product. Better than any points program or Corporate Sales Incentive Plan we went through among the Living.

Jerry and I have been on a winning streak since the cowry shells, though—assuming a week's worth of porcelain and crystal is just a Corporate oversight and not a subtle hint we need to do better. We've notched ninety-nine straight days selling through our booth. I work the register, Jerry paces, and all day long we push widgets.

"A hundred days tomorrow," I say. "That's gotta be some kind of record."

But Jerry only shrugs. "People have been doing this a long, long time."

The Food Services kid, Angelito, comes around with breakfast. He offers stale danish and a choice between lukewarm tea or "fresh" coffee that tastes like it was brewed in a Porta-John. I choose coffee because the caffeine jolt makes all of this a little more bearable.

"You hear about booth 407?" Angelito always gives us the scoop on the other exhibitors. "She dint set up yesterday. And today? She gone."

Jerry stops cranking his allen wrench. "What do you mean, gone?"

"She decided she weren't gonna sell." Angelito looks around just in case someone else might be listening. "She let her pallet sit all day, unopened. Finally Service just picked it up. All of her stock, trashed."

"And today?" I ask.

"Gone to the hot place."

Jerry's mustache twitches a little. "Don't give me that."

"I'm telling you." The kid takes off his black baseball cap and runs a hand through his hair—long, greasy. "Be careful."

He makes us swear on our mother's birthright, some kind of superstition from his homeland, that we'll exercise great caution.

And just like that the opening bell rings.

Our booth is not in the most ideal location, but I can see the heads of the first attendees pouring through the entrance. I tug my cuffs, straighten my necktie, and run a quick hand over my fly.

Jerry and I have worked 684 days in a row. The customers—attendees—change daily. I've never seen a repeat. When I was among the Living, my work conditions were such that a client might enter the store and take his or her time deciding what to purchase. But this convention hall forces us to rub elbows with the pushy, sweaty rabble—it's a third-world bazaar, on its best day. Most mornings, I have a headache before the opening bell chimes.

Jerry strides the length of our ten-foot booth saying, "Not today, man. I just can't do this today."

But pretty much right off the bat we sell 28,400 HUF worth of bric-a-brac to a woman buying Christmas gifts. I'm still scrambling to stick price tags on everything when she waltzes in, points to a stack of gilded, mouth-blown Christmas eggs, and says she'll take forty. There's a language barrier—she and the other attendees, all women, stream past the booth blathering in a tongue I've never heard. Guttural, devoid of lyricism or meter, it sounds like the language of the 15th Century Hussar cavalry. I write down a price, show her the slip. The woman says *yes* right away, which makes me think I maybe undercut myself a little, but even still it's not a bad way to start the morning.

In a 10'x10' booth there's not a lot you can do to vary your workspace. I stand on one side for a while, then I go stand on the other. My default spot is usually out in the aisle, because Jerry's older than me and likes to sit down whenever he can, and the booth looks cramped and uninviting with two grown men hanging out in it, waiting for customers like two old perverts outside on the stoop watching the neighborhood schoolgirls pass.

About an hour in, a hugely obese woman with a monstrous Labrador squeezes herself into the booth. The dog whips its tail back and forth like a windshield wiper. I can just see one of those bedazzled liqueur glasses or the gold-leafed teapots taking a nosedive. The powers-that-be hate it when our drawer is short, but they also hate shrinkage (yes, customers still steal, even here—we're not in Heaven, after all), but damaged products—especially products damaged after shipment—are completely unacceptable. As a result, I find myself trailing the dog in a half-crouch, arms outstretched, as if I'm ready to catch a projectile bowel movement from its hindquarters.

"Is this authentic?" The woman breathes kind of funny. She's got eyelashes like ferns and white chin whiskers. She holds two figurines: a bride and groom adorned in traditional Hungarian wedding attire. I'm so worried about the dog, the fact this woman speaks English doesn't occur to me until later.

"Absolutely," I say.

The dog's tail nips two candelabras. They rock back and forth, teetering, before I steady them.

She asks about a million other questions, only half of which I answer truthfully. The other half I invent answers to, at one point explaining in intricate, perhaps fabricated detail how the models in her hands are soft clay mixed with glass that is later fired in a kiln. I invite her to feel the difference between the hard porcelain and, for example, the softer tactility of the bone china on the table to her right. It goes like this for close to an hour. Following her lead, I describe every item in the booth. In the end, she buys nothing.

"Isn't that like some people?" I complain to Jerry once she's gone.

He shrugs. "Maybe she was a Shopper."

There's a rumor, unsubstantiated, that the higher-ups sometimes send one of their own to the exhibit floor to shop around the different booths. To make sure we're following protocol and actively pushing product.

"Why would they shop us?"

"Random," he says. "Another one of their mind-fucks."

But my experience as part of the Living taught me otherwise. When the higher-ups start sending Shoppers—or start paying attention at all—it usually means they're nervous.

I offer a theory. "It's the hype over booth 407."

"Possibly."

"We deserve better."

"We do."

Lunch arrives in little cardboard boxes. Angelito doesn't say much. Recent events have him spooked. He hands us our lunches and then, leaving his cart in the aisle, takes a bundle from below the warming tray.

"*Ven*," he says. "Closer."

We stand close enough to smell his cinnamon bubblegum. He hides two uncooked eggs beneath a towel.

"There is bad *joojoo* here today." He waves the eggs over us in the pattern of a cross. He produces two Styrofoam cereal bowls, pours water in both, and breaks an egg into each.

"Tonight," he says, "before you go to sleep, take some packing material and cover the bowls with it. You need to sleep with these bowls next to your heads."

"Next to our heads?" Jerry asks.

"What is this?" I want to know.

"This," Angelito says, "will keep you safe."

"Superstitious little prick," Jerry says once he's gone.

"Maybe that's why he landed here," I say. "He never learned to let go of that homeland voodoo."

Jerry shoves his bowl beneath the six-foot counter, where it might stay for a year before he remembers he put it there. He opens his turkey sandwich, flings away the wet slices of tomato, the limp lettuce, and takes a bite.

"See, that's where you and I disagree," he says. "You think this place—the attendees, Service, guys like Angelito—are here for their own reasons. That we're all sent here, wherever here is, some sort of holding pattern for the afterlife, because we all in some way failed the ultimate spiritual test."

I tear the mayonnaise packet with my teeth and spit it out. "More or less."

"But this is my afterlife." Jerry crumples his cellophane into a little ball. "You are all just figments of my defiantly agnostic imagination."

Jerry was here when I arrived. He'd been running the booth solo.

"What's the last thing you remember?" he asked when I woke up that first morning.

"A dinner party." I blinked against the fluorescents overhead. "My son-in-law was across the table. I dropped my fork."

Jerry diagnosed a heart attack. "Happens all the time. Well, that, or your son-in-law shot you down."

I considered my son-in-law: the rafting guide, the animal lover, the vegan. I didn't think he'd so much as harmed an ant in all his years on Earth. Karmically speaking, he had the Golden Ticket. I couldn't pin murder on him, much as I might have liked to.

Later I asked Jerry what was the last thing he remembered. He ignored the question and continues to hedge each time I ask. Now it's gotten so I ask just to get under his skin a little. I figure whatever it is, it's too terrible to talk about: his entire family drowned in a boating accident; a fall into the header of a tractor combine; him stoned by an angry mob.

Post-lunch, I stroll the exhibit hall and say *hello* to other vendors. There's Deborah in 124 who says the last thing she remembers is passing an eighteen-wheeler on the highway. Tyler, in 219, was, like me, a salesman of sorts among the Living and says the last thing he remembers is the taste of a .357 in his mouth. Tragic endings are more the norm around here than the exception, perhaps a common result for spiritual waffling. Shooting the breeze with the other vendors is about the only thing that makes me feel normal.

But no one's in the mood to talk. Everyone's on edge. I visit the two Irish priests in 406, across the aisle from the fated booth. They seem to be doing pretty well for themselves: today they're peddling seedlings and spongy potting soil carved into different shapes. By merely adding water, a customer can grow bean sprouts in the shape of a hippopotamus, or parsley in the outline of a crucifix.

"She lost it," one of them says of the woman who ran booth 407. "All yesterday she sat there staring at nothing."

"So what happened to her?" I ask.

"Up," one says.

"Down," the other says.

"Either way, she's out of here," the first says.

I feel sick to my stomach. "And last night?"

"I didn't hear nothing," the second says.

The first agrees. "We all went to sleep as normal, and in the morning, her booth was empty."

Leaving the 400 aisle, I take a hard left, wave to Tasha in 233 (last memory: hornets), and return to our booth. But I've left Jerry too long alone at the register. He's shaking and sweating. An angry queue has formed. I tell him to take a break and, for the next forty-five minutes, set about shortening the line. When the rush finally ends, when I finally look up from the register, most of our booth has sold.

We are talented salesmen, Jerry and I. According to him, he was top car salesman in the state twelve years running. This was back in Nebraska. Me, I became so accomplished that, in the years before my passing, a customer would enter my showroom—I was selling suits at Hart Schaffner Marx—and I'd know exactly who they were, what they needed, and how they needed to be spoken to before they ever said a word. There was no hard sell, no yammering. I'd simply match the talk and the product to the person.

But if I'd been subjected to this back among the Living, I'd have done something wildly different with my career. Here, in the exhibit hall, there's no poetry to the sales we make, no ultimate moment when the customer and I realize together that I've handed him exactly what he's been looking for. The way my clients would turn to see themselves in the mirror wearing a hand-tailored suit for the first time and not realize at first they were staring at a reflection of themselves—those were the moments that kept me going.

Sales is a service industry. But not here. In Limbo, sales is a wild frenzy of boundless greed. And every day I spend in it, a little part of me dies. Or would, if I wasn't already dead.

Jerry returns, looking like the break hasn't done him any good. His face has a waxy sheen. He makes a wheezing noise through his nose.

"Two more booths," he says. "Vanished."

No one has ever disappeared in the middle of the day. "They didn't want to work?"

He shakes his head. "Shoppers."

So he was right—there were Shoppers on the floor this morning. The perspiring woman with the Labrador was no doubt one. My sales associate is short on details, but says he watched two security guards escort a vendor through Concessions and out a double-bolted steel door.

"And another thing," he says.

I gesture for him to go on. After a moment he steps back, squats down as if his knees are made of sheet metal, and drags a two-foot by four-foot box out from underneath the table.

The box is unopened. The sturdy packing tape around the outside gleams and taunts. I approach with the caution of someone coming up on the scene of a deadly accident on the freeway. "Jerry, what is this?"

"I'm sorry," he says quickly. "It got mixed up with the empties. I didn't notice it until right before you got back, and then the line was so long—"

It takes me three strides to cross from one side of the booth to the other. Another three strides back, hands clenched. Thinking.

"Jerry, you were responsible for setting up all the merchandise on this side of the booth."

"I know."

"Then how the fuck can you forget to set out an entire box of wood-carved owls?"

He starts looking at the clock, saying maybe we still got time to sell through. But we don't. I know we don't. Even still, I cut open the box and drag it over to the register. There are two-dozen ornaments nested in tissue paper. I shove aside what remains of our point-of-sale display and lay out the rotund birds in four orderly rows. Afternoons are always slow and it's already 3:15. We have less than two hours before the hall closes, and these ornaments aren't going to sell before then. Jerry stumbles over, blathering on about slashing prices, blowing it out—he seems about ready to choke on his tongue. I redirect him, guide him to his seat and loosen his tie. I give him a moment, but then ask, "Jerry, what's on the other side of those steel doors?"

"I don't know."

"What's on the other side of the Exhibitor Services kiosk?"

"Please," he says. "Not so loud."

A plug of women clogs the aisle a few booths down. Otherwise we're alone. I grab his shoulders.

"What kind of a game is this?" I ask.

"It's not a game," he says. "It's the afterlife."

I pat him twice, conceding his point. "But we don't even know the rules, Jerry. We wake up each morning, sell a booth full of shit, and then go back to sleep. One day, maybe you're having an off day, you get hit by a Shopper and then that's it: vanished. And you've been doing this what, ten years? Haven't you ever asked yourself why?"

"It doesn't matter why." He's finally caught his breath. "It's just what is."

"Bullshit." I kick him on the ankle to keep his attention. "All these attendees, where do they come from? They must come from somewhere."

"No one's ever ventured past the gates."

"Jerry—"

"I'm not gonna be the first."

"We're better than this."

He stands, seems to search his pockets for something, then briskly takes a position behind the register. "Forget it, champ. I'm staying."

I follow him to the checkout counter. "So that's what a lifetime working as a used car salesman in Nebraska gets you: nuts the size of edamame. I'm sick of working with you anyway, you lout, sick of your working only just as much as you need to get by. Always sticking me at the register because you can't tell a wooden shell from a goddamn bone!"

But it's like he doesn't hear me. He stands at the register, hands in his pockets, staring out at the aisle. Salesmen, the good ones, are chameleons. We blend with our environment, the shelves of folded sweaters, the glass counters stuffed with diamonds, so that we can hover in close proximity to a customer without his noticing. So that when we see a client making the decision to purchase, we're on it in a snap. As I turn to leave, Jerry has disappeared: he's the color of industrial cash registers, of wire endcaps, the washed-out gray of the cement floor.

A commotion three booths down: two security guards escorting yet another vendor from the exhibit hall. They're fierce-looking—black-glass visors hide their faces. But one of them turns his head, and I know immediately that we've made eye contact. Cold shivers run up my neck, behind my ear. And then he's pointing at me even as I'm scrambling around our last table and out of our booth, in the opposite direction.

The closest exit is the 200 aisle, a set of double doors past the Retracta-belt posts. A few attendees mingle in the corral. They don't notice me until I'm right on top of them. Someone shouts my name—I slide beneath the belt-fence and, my dress shoes slipping at the heels and smacking against the cold tile, bumble toward the exit.

Six-hundred, eighty-four days. This is the only number that matters. Sixteen-thousand-four-hundred-and-sixteen hours I've spent peddling macramé plant hangers, tins of foie gras, live sugar bears—half of which were dead when we unwrapped the pallet. Maybe it's paradise on the other side of the doors, or maybe it's an inferno. Or something else, something unimaginable. But I'm not waiting around for either me or Jerry or both of us to crack up.

I hit the exit. The handle collapses. The door swings open. I trip into a wide, carpeted hall. Escalators going down: I take two steps at a time to the lower level, imagining daylight, a cool breeze against my armpits, the way my throat will burn gulping fresh air. But the next level reveals another carpeted hall with exhibit doors on both sides. Another set of escalators down: I take these, too. And the next, when they appear. And the next. Down six escalators, then eight, then twelve. Finding each time the same carpet, vaguely reddish with shield-shapes of yellow and black; the same polished aluminum steps; the same system of whirring belts on the same continuous loop. The signs never change. An arrow points down, *Next Level Down*. An arrow points up, *Next Level Up*. There are no placards for restrooms, exits, or parking. Up or down. Two choices. What could be simpler? I choose down until I lose count.

Winded, knees complaining, eventually I stop. I'm on a level just like my own, just like the hundred or more that have preceded it. There are escalators in the center of the hall and on either side wide, double doors reading *Exhibit Hall A* and *Exhibit Hall B*. I choose a door and push through. It is a convention center hall much like mine but not exactly mine. The attendees are children mostly; a different woman runs the Exhibitor Services kiosk; from where I stand I can see booth 124 and it is not Deborah but a man who looks like a college professor wearing a beard and yarmulke.

If I walked to my own booth, 523, it would not be Jerry but someone else, perhaps two people, the second being my doppelgänger in this particular Exhibit Hall A, on this particular level, amongst potentially infinite levels.

Suddenly, I feel incredibly homesick. Not for my place among the Living, but for my booth upstairs, so far away now, and Jerry, in the exhibit hall I've come to call home.

"What did you expect?" a voice asks.

A kid who looks a little like Angelito, but who is not Angelito, stands beside me, hands drumming on his empty lunch cart. He wears a blue baseball cap. His skin is lighter, although they speak the same, streetwise. This is a version of the kid who delivers our meals, but on this particular convention center floor instead of ours.

"Don't worry, bro," he says. "We got you covered. Angelito radioed down and said you was heading our way."

"How many?" I mean to ask how many levels, how many booths in this complex of exhibit halls, but I sense the number might be so staggering, infinite perhaps, that I can't bring myself to say the words.

"Don't ask." He lays a hand on my shoulder. "C'mon. I'll take you back up."

I count the floors up this time: 171.


For the seventh day in a row, our register balanced. And our streak is intact: we sold through our booth. The irony, of course, is that if they come for me tonight because I made a break for it, there was really no need. We sold through. As always. Because Jerry and I are pros.

We're ready for tomorrow. Except that it's unlikely there will be a tomorrow, for me, in this exhibit hall.

"Already this smells rotten." Jerry has taken Angelito's advice and covered his egg and water bowl with packing peanuts. We are both of us in our cots, waiting, the day's final conversation, a few more minutes to force past with small-talk. The last rinse of water down an empty sink.

"You sold the entire booth without me here," I say. "See? You still got it."

"I guess so."

"I'm sorry I called you a coward."

"Think nothing of it."

"Will they give you a new partner?"

"I hope not."

Jerry didn't ask what I saw while I was gone, and I don't have the heart to tell him. Maybe he suspects, as I now know, that there is only one dimension here and only one way to measure time.

But Infinity is hard to get your mind around, even when you're living it.

Slowly, the lights go out. We hear the whoosh of them shutting off at the far end of the hall. We watch the shadows encroach. The lights above our booth hiss and shudder and then the exhibit hall is black. Only the clock casts a red-tinted halo, each night the same time when I close my eyes and try to sleep: 10:00. The colon flashes, steadily measuring out seconds that, in the end, measure nothing.

"I'm excited." I know Jerry is awake because I can't hear him snoring. "You know, good or bad, I'll find out what's after this. And maybe there's nothing after this. But you know, I've been thinking, maybe they'll just move me to a different hall."

"Afraid not," Jerry says. I wait for him to go on but It's a long time coming. When he speaks again it sounds as if he's transmitting from the wrong side of the booth, or from out in the aisle, instead of where he usually sleeps. The sensation is disorienting, and I wonder if there's an echo in here I've never noticed.

"I told you I used to be a car salesman," he says.

"Car salesman of the year, twelve years running," I say back to him.

"Yeah, well." He clears his throat. "What I said about that may not have been exactly true. In fact, you might say I never had a life among the Living at all."

My heartbeat picks up a little, but I won't move—even though it sounds like Jerry's voice is everywhere at once.

"In fact, no one here did. Or no one here did but you."

This isn't Jerry's voice—it sounds like Angelito. But why is he serving food this late?

There's a metallic taste on the back of my tongue. "What are you telling me, Jerry?"

"Look pal, don't worry," he says. "Just close your eyes. Tomorrow, everything will be different."

"Jerry—"

But he won't answer me. In another minute, I hear him snoring. I've always hated the way he can fall asleep so easily, as if he hasn't a care in the world. I realize now he never has—not in any world I've known, anyway.

I can feel sleep tugging behind my eyes, wrapping my ankles, curling like a genuine mink tail over the back of my head. In a booth nearby, someone coughs. Someone else kicks a counter leg in their sleep and the leg makes a harsh sound scraping against the floor. Several people stir, and then the hall falls quiet again.

# Catherine Jacobi

### EVERYDAY OBJECTS AND MAKING POETRY

This work has been influenced by poet Richard Wilbur's comment about writing poetry.

"I do think it's almost always true that a poem begins when two things, perhaps an inner thing and an outer thing which hadn't been together before, suddenly converge and feel as if they wanted to make something new."

In this work, everyday objects from the simplest and most overlooked places reference basic human nature and anatomy. Years of collected newspapers, photos, kitchen tables and chairs, outboard propellers, and baby shoes, all bound to be discarded or at the very least dismissed, leverage the "something new."

Starting these conversations in the vernacular engages what one already knows, juxtaposes, and constructs. It is a common commentary that the constancy of objects, which endure in our memories, only ever changes.

## *Advice to a Prophet*

2017

tree branch, outboard propeller   32" x 18" x 18"

*Doll*

2021

Mrs. Beasley Doll, wax  20" x 8" x 5"

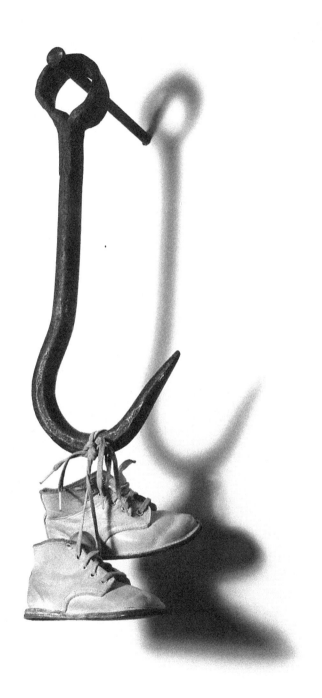

**Tender Hooks**

2017

meat hook, baby shoes  18" x 6" x 3"

### *Label*
2020
magazine photo, name labels  16" x 12

Christine Sneed
# *The Monkey's Uncle Louis*

Louis's younger sister Anne had adopted a monkey, news she shared with him over the phone, her call waking him early on a Tuesday morning, on the first day of the fall semester. She wanted to know if he'd like to come to Florida to meet the monkey. It was a white-bellied capuchin, a female. She was very sweet-natured, smart, and funny. Anne sounded smitten, a little dazed, the happiest she'd sounded in a while.

"I suppose I could," he said. "The first few weeks of the term aren't too busy." He could hear noises in the background, a series of beeps followed by laughter. "What's her name?" he asked.

"Bill and I haven't decided yet," said Anne. "I'll send you an email with the names we're considering."

"All right. If you want to."

"You're not happy for us," she said flatly.

"That's not true. I am happy for you," he said. "You sound good."

"I'm glad you think so."

Before they hung up he asked, "Is it legal to have a monkey in Florida? Don't you need a permit or something?"

His sister hesitated, a sound escaping her throat that he'd been familiar with since childhood. She was trying not to cry. "Yes, of course. We have one, Louis. We're not criminals."

The email with the proposed monkey names arrived that evening while he was eating dinner alone in an Olive Garden near his house. He only cooked on weekends when his wife was home. Nearly every Friday, she flew back to Chicago from Hartford where she worked as a hospital administrator, or he flew to her. They'd been making these trips for six of the nine years they'd been married. Louis was a tenured professor in American history at a college three miles from their house, and when Sandra was hired by the hospital in Hartford, they'd both agreed his job was too good to give up with its summers off and generous pension and periodic sabbaticals. They had a cat, Jules, but no children; Jules was Sandra's cat and pre-dated Louis, although the cat lived in Chicago instead of Hartford. In the last year, Jules had developed diabetes, and in Sandra's absence, it was Louis who administered the insulin shots, the cat submitting to them with disappointment on his owlish face, his tail flicking back and forth while Louis inserted the needle under the skin behind his neck. His disappointment was even plainer when he peered each morning into his food bowl: the vet had put him on a special diet, one with more protein but less flavor.

Dear Louis,

Here are the names we're thinking about for our monkey. Can you rank them from 1 to 5, with 1 being your first choice and send them back to me?
Lucinda
Molly
Jeannie
Becky
Claire

Bill and I would love it if you'd come down the next weekend you're free—what about Labor Day? If Sandra isn't planning to be in Hartford that weekend, maybe she can come too.

Love, Anne

P.S. We are already so in love with our little monkey!

He had misgivings about his sister's plan to make a home for a wild creature that was likely soon to bring its new keepers to their knees. What would happen if in the middle of the night the monkey escaped the house, and homesick for its native jungle, started screeching from the treetops and rattling neighbors' doors and windows?

Online he found a video of a gang of capuchins chasing after four fawn-colored Chihuahuas, someone off-screen laughing maniacally. The Chihuahuas looked terrified, their eyes bulging even more than Louis thought was normal. The monkeys screamed and pogoed up and down when they overtook the horrified dogs.

Another video showed a tufted capuchin feverishly pulling socks and underwear out of a chest of drawers and flinging them over its shoulders.

Dear Anne,
Just curious, do monkeys like bananas as much as they say?

Of the names you sent, I think I like Lucinda the best, Claire probably the least (it's a nice enough name but maybe not quite right for a monkey?). I don't really have strong feelings about the other three names, but I suppose Molly would be my second choice.

I'll see what Sandra is able to do regarding a visit. Labor Day might work.

Hello to Bill from both of us.

Your brother, Louis

P.S. I guess this makes me the monkey's uncle.

At first Sandra didn't believe him when he called to share his sister's news. "I'm too tired tonight for jokes," she said.

"It's not a joke," he said. "Anne and Bill really have adopted a monkey."

There was a long pause before she said, "Can they return it?"

"I don't know. I didn't ask."

"What's wrong with a dog?"

"Nothing," he said. "But apparently they wanted a monkey."

"I don't think I can change my plane ticket for next weekend without a big penalty," she said. "What if you go the weekend after Labor Day when I'll be here? Or we could meet down there the following weekend."

"I'll check with my sister. I do think we should both go."

"What if that monkey gets into our room in the middle of the night?" she asked. "I don't know if I'll be able to sleep."

"I'll protect you."

"We'll see," she said.

"Which name do you like best?" he asked. "Claire, Lucinda, Molly, Jeannie or Becky? Anne wants to know."

His wife was silent for a second. "Your sister has lost her mind."

The monkey, who Anne and Bill had named Molly, stared worriedly at Louis from her perch on Bill's shoulder when he and Sandra arrived at the front door of her new home. She was dressed in a diaper and a pink T-shirt with Daddy's Girl in cursive on the front, a chunk of mango oozing in one of her small hands. She was tinier than Louis expected, at most five pounds. Jules weighed ten. The monkey's head and chest were blond-furred; the rest of her was covered in brown fur. She made a hissing noise and bared her teeth, revealing two sharp-looking fangs. Sandra hung back, hesitating. Louis put his hand on her arm.

"Oh, don't worry, she's harmless," said Anne with a nervous laugh. "Such a little love." She caressed the monkey's miniature head. Ducking away from Anne's hand, Molly continued to stare distrustfully at Louis and his wife.

Bill and Anne stepped away from the door and led them into the front room, the monkey craning its neck to keep its eyes on them. "I've put you in your usual room," said Anne. "It's right next to Molly's."

"Molly has her own room?" asked Sandra. She looked at Louis in alarm.

"Don't say anything," he mouthed.

They passed the living room where a large playpen had been installed in the space between the sofa and the television cabinet. Wooden alphabet blocks, a large plastic pineapple, a one-eyed Mr. Potato Head, and a constellation of small stuffed animals—frogs, kittens, and two monkeys that resembled Molly—were scattered in and around the playpen. Louis wondered how long it would take the monkey to start hurling the blocks at the windows or her new parents. Next to the television crouched a stuffed monkey much larger than the two on the floor.

"Of course she has her own room!" said Anne. "We didn't want her to get into the habit of sleeping in ours, but she does come in sometimes in the middle of the night, wanting to cuddle."

Bill looked at his wife. "I think we're going to have to start locking our bedroom door when we turn in."

Anne shook her head, her dark curls bobbing. "No, no, we can't do that. Molly won't like that."

Sandra glanced at Louis again, but he pretended not to notice. "She's very cute," he said. "Very precocious too, it sounds like."

"Yes, she's extremely bright," said Anne. "The breeder we got her from up near Orlando told us she's one of the smartest monkeys he's ever known."

"Maybe she'll ace the SATs and get into Harvard by the time she's 12," said Sandra.

Anne didn't laugh but out of loyalty to his wife, Louis did. "That's funny," he said.

"I thought so," said Sandra.

"I hope she gets a scholarship," said Bill. "I don't think we could afford any of the Ivies."

Molly finished the mango and let out a deafening shriek. Bill winced and put a hand over his right ear. "Ah, Molly, no. I told you not to do that." He tried to catch the monkey's eye but she leapt off his shoulder onto Anne's head and covered Anne's eye sockets with her small, deft hands, at least one of them sticky with mango juice. With an embarrassed laugh, Anne tried to pry the monkey loose, but Molly refused to be dislodged.

"Take it easy on her," said Bill, putting a cautioning hand on Molly's back. "You know she doesn't like it when you do that."

Molly blinked up at him and opened her mouth but no sounds emerged. Louis eyed her fangs; he doubted his sister was considering having them filed down.

"I need a nap," said Sandra. "Would anyone object?"

"No, go right ahead," said Anne, still blind. "We can all take Molly to the beach this afternoon. I need to make her lunch now, and I have sandwich fixings for you whenever you're ready."

Louis looked from Anne to the monkey, sensing they were both suffering in very personal ways; Bill also seemed tired and dispirited. Louis was certain that living with his sister required more stoicism than he himself would have been capable of. Anne was almost pathologically thin-skinned and anxious, but his brother-in-law, for reasons he and Sandra had speculated over many times, remained committed. His own marriage, Louis supposed, was doubtless a source of speculation for Anne and Bill too.

"Lock the door," said Sandra after they were alone in their room, one of its dusky pink walls streaked above the baseboard with what looked like dried mud. "That monkey must know how to use a doorknob if she sneaks into their room at night."

"She's cute," he said. "Don't you think?"

His wife gave him a wry look. "Yes, she is, but what's she doing here? She's a wild animal."

"Don't say that so loud," he said. "They can probably hear us."

"Good, because they should listen to what I'm saying."

He shook his head. "Don't be cranky. You didn't have to come."

Sandra snorted. "You told me I had to."

"I didn't say you had to. I just thought it would be a good idea if you did."

"That's basically the same thing," she said, flopping down onto the bed. She sat up again a second later, her expression pinched, and groped under the pillow. "What is this?" she said, pulling out two very brown and squashed bananas. "The monkey's secret stash?"

He laughed. "I guess they weren't kidding about how smart she is."

Sandra looked disgusted. "I knew this would be a bad idea." She thrust a hand under the other pillow and extracted a third banana, this one blacker than the other two. "How long do you think this has been here?" She waved the black banana at him.

"Probably no more than three weeks. I think that's how long they've had her." He went over to the streaks on the wall and bent down to sniff them. "Smells like banana," he said.

"Wonderful," said Sandra. She got up and dropped the squashed fruit into a trashcan by the dresser. "I think we're going to have to ask Anne to change the sheets. I'm not sleeping in a bed that smells like rotten bananas. We're lucky there aren't any fruit flies."

Somewhere in the house they heard the monkey screeching. "I hope your sister has gotten that creature off her head by now," said Sandra.

"I think we'd better tell them about the sheets a little later," he said.

Anne had a rainbow-colored leash for the monkey and a matching harness, which she assured Louis they'd be using at the beach. Molly sat quietly on Anne's lap as Bill drove them toward the ocean, Louis next to Sandra in the backseat, the air conditioner not cooling down the car fast enough; he'd already sweated through his T-shirt and could feel his boxers bunching against his groin. A half open diaper bag sat on the hump between him and Sandra; inside he could see two Ziploc bags bulging with Cheerios and Goldfish crackers, two juice boxes and several diapers. There was also a tiny pair of pink socks and what looked like a onesie. He wondered who among his sister's and Bill's friends had been introduced to the monkey, and if any of Anne's friends had thrown her a shower. He hoped so, but didn't ask. Sandra would think he was a lunatic and chastise him later.

"Uncle Louis," said Sandra, noticing where he was looking. "Don't steal your niece's Goldfish. I see you eyeballing them."

"Don't you dare eat those," said Anne. She'd put on some make-up, red lipstick and black mascara, and had tied up her hair in a yellow bandanna, over which she'd placed a pair of sunglasses, large black ones that covered half her face.

"I'm not going to eat them," he said. "Sandra's trying to get me in trouble."

His wife pursed her lips. "If you thought you could get away with it, you'd eat them."

"You need to bring him some snacks of his own," said Bill, meeting Sandra's eyes in the rearview mirror. "Anne brought me a Power Bar."

"I brought us all Power Bars," Anne said primly.

"That was nice of you," said Sandra, who Louis knew didn't like energy bars of any kind. Neither of them had mentioned the rotten bananas or the sheets yet. Sandra was waiting for him to do it, but he was stalling, certain it would spoil their beach trip.

The afternoon was punishingly hot, the air torpid with humidity, the fronds of the palm trees bordering the streets limp in the sun. Anne had warned him that September was sometimes as unbearable as August. Most years he and Sandra visited at Thanksgiving or Christmas, the weather in Hartford and Chicago by that point reliably bad. He and his sister were all that remained of their close family; their mother had died two years earlier, their father ten years before her. Bill had grown up in Ft. Lauderdale, and his parents and one of his two brothers still lived nearby. Louis doubted that any of them had met the monkey—Anne didn't like her in-laws, who she thought blamed her for their lack of grandchildren. Bill's brothers were bachelors; one was gay, the other, who was secretive and out of touch for months at a time, was anyone's guess, according to Anne.

"Will it be too hot for Molly at the beach?" asked Sandra.

"Oh, no, no," said Anne. "She has family in the jungles of Costa Rica. She loves the heat. The beach is one of her favorite places."

"I'm guessing you've taken her down here already," said Louis.

"Every day we can manage it," said Anne.

"Nine times now," said Bill, glancing at Anne. "I think."

"But who's counting?" said Sandra under her breath.

Louis elbowed her side. She looked at him and shook her head, smiling.

If Anne or Bill had heard her, they gave no sign. Bill was slowing down to park the minivan, a white behemoth purchased with optimism three years earlier in anticipation of a human baby. Louis had asked his sister the previous Christmas if she and Bill were considering adoption, but Anne said they weren't. "If we can't have a baby of our own, we don't want one." After a pause, she'd added, "He'd probably be willing to adopt, but I don't want to." She'd had three miscarriages in four years; she was 43 and a former heavy smoker, which her doctor thought might be partly responsible for the miscarriages. Bill was 46, the same age as Louis. He'd never smoked, but he sometimes joked that he liked smoked meats, which Anne did not find funny.

Louis and Sandra didn't want children, which for reasons that weren't clear to him his sister resented. ("It's because we haven't been through any of the same difficulties she has," Sandra insisted. "If we wanted kids too, she'd feel better." But he didn't think this made sense. "If we wanted kids and went on to have them," he said, "she'd feel even worse, wouldn't she?" "Not necessarily," said Sandra. "It's not logical. Not at all.")

The glare from the sand scraped at Louis's eyes, despite his polarized sunglasses. Sandra had insisted he pack a hat too and he'd also brought her sun hat, a wide-brimmed straw one that made her look girlish and unattainable. She was two years older than Anne but with her unlined olive skin and trimmer figure, she looked several years younger. Louis had spent the summer with her in Hartford, and they were both still adjusting to his return to Chicago for the start of the school year. She'd been searching for a comparable job in Illinois but hadn't yet found one, despite having made it to the final round of interviews for several. The positions had all gone to men, she'd eventually discovered and been furious over, Louis commiserating in his own disappointment over these hirings. The trend wasn't the same in the history department or the others he was familiar with at the college; most of the new jobs were going to women. Sandra had had a startlingly caustic response to this disclosure: "I'm sure there are more women in those applicant pools than in mine. Most men don't want university teaching jobs," she said. "For one, they don't pay very much. No offense to you, Louis, but you know it's true."

Anne was trying to clip the leash to Molly's harness, the monkey shrieking and skittering from her lap to Bill's in her excitement. Bill grabbed the monkey and held her determinedly while Anne attached the leash.

"Can you bring the diaper bag?" Bill asked over his shoulder.

"Sure," said Louis, reaching for it, but Sandra snatched it first and slung it over her shoulder. He followed her out of the van, biting back a complaint.

Friday afternoon and the beach was festooned with umbrellas and clusters of chairs on which oiled-up, exhausted parents reclined, dazed by the heat, their children scattered around them, digging energetically in the sand or else sobbing over some recent affront. Molly rode into the melee on Bill's shoulders, children's heads turning when they spotted her, their excavations paused.

"A monkey!" several of them cried before dropping their plastic shovels and running over. The children twirled and danced around Molly and her parents on sandy, sun-browned feet, pointing up at her, their faces transfigured by joy.

Molly stared down at them from her regal height with what looked to Louis like scorn. The monkey blinked and turned to Anne, who stepped closer and put a protective hand on her tiny blonde head. In the next second, the monkey sprang from Bill's shoulders onto Anne's head and worked her little hands beneath Anne's sunglasses, covering her eyes in a repeat of what had happened at the house. The kids' laughter at this maneuver grew hysterical. Sandra stood a few feet away, covering her mouth with one hand to muffle her laughter, taking it all in. Louis tried to catch her eye.

"I want to pet the monkey," cried a little girl in a pink swimsuit, her belly a large hard balloon. Louis watched her stare commandingly at Bill and Anne, admiring her a little. She was still years away from self-consciousness and its inconveniences.

A little boy with black hair and a skinny girl in a ruffled blue swimsuit made the same demand. "I love monkeys," said the boy. "Let me pet him!"

"Me too," cried the girl, both arms raised toward Anne and the monkey. "I want to pet him."

"She's a girl," said Anne. "Her name is Molly."

"Molly," said the girl in the ruffled swimsuit. She giggled. "That's my mom's name."

A second little boy asked if he could please touch the monkey's tail.

Louis saw Bill grimace before Sandra spoke up from behind. "Come on, you guys. You have to let them pet the monkey. Why else bring her here?"

Bill turned to Sandra with a harassed look as he tried to free his wife's eyes from the monkey's grip. "Molly is very excitable," he said. "We need to give her time to adjust to her new surroundings." He looked pointedly at the children. "Give us about fifteen minutes. Why don't you go back to your sandcastles for now?"

"You said that the last time we saw you," said the girl in the pink swimsuit. "But you left before you let us pet her."

Sandra laughed in a hard burst.

"I'm sure if we—" said Louis, looking at Bill.

"For God's sake," cried Anne from behind the monkey's hands. "Help me!"

Molly screeched as Bill tried with more force to pry her loose from his wife. When at last he succeeded, the monkey leapt onto his head and was about to clap her hands over his eyes when Bill grabbed them and lifted her squirming hirsute body away from his face. "Molly, no," he said, exasperated. "How many times have we told you you can't keep doing that?"

"Does she understand you?" asked one of the little boys.

"Apparently not," said Sandra. "Or else she's decided to ignore them."

"You think this is all very funny," said Anne, her face blanched with fury. "But it's not. This is our life!"

"I was only making a little joke," said Sandra, taken aback. "I'm sorry if I offended you."

"You've been making your little jokes at our expense since you and Louis got here, and they're not funny at all," said Anne. "You can see very well just how hard this is."

"I think we need to change Molly's diaper," Bill said ominously.

"Then do it," said Anne through gritted teeth. She yanked the diaper bag from Sandra's shoulder and thrust it at her husband. Molly bared her teeth.

"Stop it," said Anne. "You're being very naughty, Molly!"

"Do you think we should go home?" asked Louis.

Bill and his sister stared at him, chagrined. "I—I just thought it might be a good idea," he mumbled.

"No," said Anne. "We're not going home yet. Molly needs her beach time."

The kids went back to their shovels and pails without another word, cowed by Anne's outburst. One of their mothers had removed her sunglasses and was glaring at Bill, but he didn't notice. Anne was ordering him to put down a towel and change the monkey's diaper as he struggled to keep Molly away from his face. "You do it," he said. "You can see very well that I have my hands full right now."

Sandra came up beside Louis and gripped his elbow. "I'm sorry if I offended your sister," she whispered. "But she's going to need a better sense of humor if she expects them to survive this whole thing. Bill too."

The monkey squirmed free of Bill's grip and leapt onto the sand, more children turning to stare at her in electrified amazement. Anne was still holding the leash and ran after Molly in her flight toward the water. Near the shoreline, her sagging diaper fell off and some of the children screamed with laughter. With a cry of distress, Anne jerked the leash to stop Molly and bent down to pick up the diaper before the tide carried it away.

"Calm down, Molly," she said. "You're acting like you've never been here before."

Before Anne stood up, the monkey jumped onto her back and pressed her hands over Anne's eye sockets again. Louis winced as his sister released a great howl of frustration.

Bill stared down at the sand, his mouth a grim line, before he went over to his wife and picked up the soiled diaper from where she'd dropped it by her feet. He glanced at Louis helplessly.

"I'm sorry," said Louis.

Bill didn't reply.

"I think she's overstimulated," said Anne in a strained voice. "She's not used to sharing us with strangers for so long."

No one wanted to talk on the ride home. Sandra scrolled through email on her phone and Louis fell asleep with his head against the window, his right hand resting on his wife's warm thigh. His neck was stiff by the time Bill turned into the driveway and jolted him awake.

"Slow down," said Anne. "Are you trying to kill us?" Molly chittered from her lap and looked imperiously up at Bill.

"Come on," he said. "I wasn't going that fast."

In the house, Sandra went directly to their room but Louis lingered in the den, knowing he needed to mention the sheets. Bill muttered something about a shower and left them alone with the monkey.

"I know what you're thinking," said Anne from the sofa she'd collapsed onto. Molly was in her playpen, denuding the Mr. Potato Head and tossing the pieces aside.

"What?" asked Louis.

"That we've bitten off more than we can chew."

"I wasn't thinking that," he said.

"I was," she said, morose.

"Do you have to keep her?"

Anne was silent for several seconds. "No, we don't, but I want to," she finally said, her look imploring.

"You're sure?"

She nodded. "I think we can make it work if we're committed."

"Does Bill think so too?"

She leaned her head back against the sofa. "I don't know."

After a moment Louis said, "Don't you think you should ask him?"

Her mascara was smeared beneath her eyes, her lipstick long gone. The monkey's presence had drained her in a way Louis hadn't expected—he was used to her air of aggrieved injury when she was upset, but now she only seemed sad and luckless. "It's only been a few weeks," she said softly. "He's just taking longer to adjust than I am."

"Have you adjusted?"

She nodded. "Yes. She's the light of my life."

Louis had to look away from her beseeching gaze.

"I know it's hard to believe, but most of the time she's very sweet and well-behaved."

"That's good," he said. "I want you to be happy."

Anne started to cry. "But I didn't think this would be so hard." She wiped roughly at her cheeks.

"Are you sure you should keep her? Really sure?" he asked, stricken.

"Yes," she said. "I'm keeping her no matter what."


An hour after midnight, he was still awake, having refused Sandra's offer of a sleeping pill. Out in the yard, a bird he couldn't identify began singing, another bird answering from farther away. When it was quiet again, he heard the monkey push open the door to her room. Sandra had asked at dinner if they'd thought about keeping her in a cage at night, but Anne said they weren't willing to treat their monkey like a prisoner. Molly would eventually get used to sleeping through the night on her own. No one expected a human baby to sleep for more than a few hours at a time right after coming home from the hospital—why should they expect a baby monkey to be any different?

Louis slipped out of bed, Sandra murmuring and turning onto her side as he left the room. At the far end of the hall, he could see Molly turning the knob of Bill and Anne's bedroom door, but it didn't open. Anne opened it after a few seconds, her white nightgown phosphorescent in the glow from the hall nightlight. Molly leapt into her arms, and Louis, overcome by shame, watched his sister press her face to the monkey's soft head, both she and Molly closing their eyes in ecstatic surrender.

*photo by Carma Lynn Park*

# Katherine Ace

The intersection of contraries fascinates me: life and death; humor and tragedy; beauty and corruption; natural and constructed realities; experience and news. I am captivated by complex issues that we all face, and yet experience personally, intimately. I am interested in the role of dark feelings, thoughts and states of mind in the process of transformation. I am drawn to fire beneath reserve.

I think of painting as a dynamic process, expressing energy through the coupling of opposites. The raw canvas is both filled and completely empty. Akin to dreaming, I begin with an image in mind but I am not clear how it will manifest. I do not derive my imagery from sleeping dreams but from my eyes, my imagination, my memory, as well as photography, historical references and chance. These together construct the "whole." In process, I pursue a dynamic interaction between intuitive images, a sensual and physical handling of the paint, and the spirit or accident of the moment.

Although stylistically I incorporate representation, paradoxically, I approach the canvas abstractly and employ gesture founded in Abstract Expressionism. I throw paint at the canvas and sculpt the surface using painting knives, nails, pins, bottle brushes, gold leaf, plastic, anything that is lying around. I work whatever my mood, and each piece combines the intentional with the accidental, the textured layers forming what becomes the body and flesh of the painting.

I am interested in complex story telling. Figures and still lifes evolve as open ended metaphors/allegories for concepts and environments that are themselves also metaphors/allegories, and therefore fold, like fabric, time or paint, back in on themselves. Like a poem, a painting is a surface. The depth is in the surface (oddly). It sort of dawns on you – like the way one remembers a dream sometimes, in fragments that float up all through the day, assembling themselves oddly, disturbingly...

***Juniper Tree***
2013

*Great Awakening Under*
2013

*Faclcon and Falconner*
2018

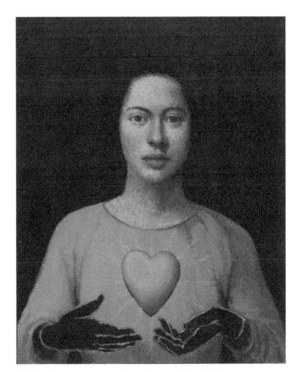

*Madonna of the Lost Souls*
2018

*Grandma*
2016

*Fitcher's Feathered Bird with Tiny Tree*
2014

Libby Fischer Hellman

# *Your Sweet Man*

"Who's Gonna Be Your Sweet Man When I'm gone?
Who you gonna have to love you?"
...Muddy Waters

### 1982: Chicago

Calvin waited for the man who'd been convicted of killing his mother. Outside Joliet prison the July heat seared his spirit, leaving it as bare and desiccated as a sun-bleached bone. Sweat ringed his arm pits, grit coated the back of his neck. Almost noon, and not a shadow on anything.

He extracted a Lucky from the crumpled pack on the dash and leaned forward to light it. The '74 Chevy Caprice never failed to start up. As long as he kept enough fluid in the radiator, the engine ate up the highway without complaint. Even the lighter worked.

He took a nervous drag. He hadn't seen his father in fifteen years. His granny had made him come when he graduated high school to show him that Calvin had amounted to something, after all. Calvin remembered clutching his diploma in the visitors' room, sliding it out of the manila envelope, edging nervously up to the glass window that separated them. He held it up against the glass, hating the sour smell of the place, the chipped paint on the walls, the fact that he had to be there at all. He remembered how his father nodded. No smile. No "atta boy – you done good." Just a lukewarm nod. Calvin imagined a yawning hole opening up on the floor, right then and there, a hole he could sink into and disappear.

Now, the black metal gates swung open, and a withered man emerged. Calvin was still wiping sweat off his face, but his father was wearing a long sleeved shirt and beige canvas pants. Even from a distance, his father looked smaller than he remembered. Frailer. The cancer that was consuming him, that had triggered his early release, was working its way through his body. He walked slowly, stooped over. His skin, a few shades lighter than the rich chocolate it once was, looked paper-thin, and he blinked like he hadn't been in sunlight for years. Maybe he hadn't. His father looked around, then spotted Calvin in the Caprice. He nodded, took his time coming over.

Calvin slid out of the car, tossed his cigarette on the dirt, and ground it out with his foot. "Hello, Calvin…"

Calvin returned his greeting with a nod of his own. Cautious. Polite.

"Appreciate you coming to get me, son."

A muscle in Calvin's gut twitched. He couldn't remember the last time someone had called him "son." "Son" was a word that belonged in the movies or TV, not in real life. Calvin gestured to the gym bag his father was carrying. "Let me take that."

His father held it out. Calvin threw it in the back seat. His father stood at the passenger door but made no effort to open it. Calvin frowned, then realized his father was waiting for permission. Twenty-five years in prison did that to a man. "Just open the door and get in."

His father shot him a look, half-embarrassed, half-grateful, and slid into the car. Calvin waited until his father was settled, then started the engine. As they pulled away from Joliet, he said, "Thought we'd go back to my place."

"You still in Englewood?"

"Hyde Park now. Got ourselves a house near 47th and Cottage Grove."

His father's eyebrows arched. "Well, that's mighty fine."

"Jeanine fixed it up nice. Even got a little garden out back. She's a _good_ girl."

His father didn't seem to notice. He should have. It was Jeanine who shamed him into picking him up in the first place.

"He's dying, Calvin" she'd said. "And he's paid his dues. Twenty-five years of 'em."

Now his father turned to him. "How's that job coming?"

"What job?" Calvin made his way back to the highway.

"The one you was talking about when you come to see me. Janitorial supplies."

"I opened my own company six years ago. I got five people working for me now."

"Well that's mighty fine, son. Mighty fine."

But it didn't feel fine. It felt false. Calvin imagined that black hole opening up even wider. That was why he never wrote or visited his father, except for the Christmas card Jeanine made him sign every year. Any time he thought about him, even a stray fragment, the night his mother was murdered flooded back into his mind. He couldn't help it. Better not to think about it at all, his granny would say. "Just go on and live your own life."

But Granny was dead, and the people at Joliet called _him_ when they found the cancer. Calvin stole a glance at his father. He was quiet. Just staring out at the road, a dreamy look on his face. Calvin remembered that look. His father's body might be in the front seat, but his mind was miles away. Calvin knew he was thinking about his mother. He tightened his grip on the wheel. How dare he?

"So... You feelin' okay?"

His father pulled his gaze in and looked at Calvin. "For the days I got left, I'm doing jes' fine."

Calvin turned onto the interstate. "You sure? Jeanine talked to our doctor. He can see you tomorrow if you want."

His father gave him a sad little smile. "Appreciate it son, but don't go to no trouble." His father went back to looking out the window. Calvin turned on the radio. The all news station was blaring out something about Israeli troops in Lebanon. His father didn't react, just kept gazing out. He seemed somehow smaller, less distinct than he'd been just ten minutes ago. Like his shadow was slowly fading from black to gray. At this rate he might disappear altogether.

Calvin snapped off the radio. For a while the whine of the air conditioning was the only sound in the car. Lulled by the air blowing through the vents and the rhythm of his wheels on the highway, Calvin was startled by the abruptness of his father's voice.

"You start making the arrangements?"

Calvin cleared his throat just loud enough. "Not yet." He wasn't sure what to expect. Would his father lay into him? Cuss him out?

But all his father did was to wave a weak hand. "I guess I got to do it myself."

"Why don't we talk about it later?"

His father's shoulders sagged and he closed his eyes. "I ain't got many laters, son."

## 1950s: Chicago

The hot breath of the blues kissed Jimmy Jay Rollins when he was little, leaving him hungering for more. His mama -- he never knew his daddy – took him to church in the morning and the blues joints at night. By the time he was seven, he was playing guitar licks with whoever his "uncle" of the moment happened to be, and by the time he left school at 16, he knew he wanted to play bass guitar.

The bass wasn't as flashy as the electric slide guitar of Little Ed or Muddy Waters, but it was the glue that held everything together. No one could play a 12-bar chorus without him; no one could start a lick or riff. The bass was there through every number, from beginning to end, setting the pace. Steady. Unrelenting. The lead guitar, saxophone, even the drummer could take a break; not so the bass. Willie Dixon became Jimmy Jay's personal hero.

By day, Jimmy Jay worked in a steel factory near Lake Calumet, but at night, he bounced around playing gigs on the South Side. You could smell stale cigarette smoke and yesterday's beer in the air, spot a few guns and knives if you looked real close. But none of that mattered when the music started. The blues flowed through his veins, transporting him to a place where he could let go, soar above the world, tethered only by an electric guitar, wailing horn, or harmonica riff.

He was jamming at the open mike set in the Macomba Lounge one hot summer night, a thick cloud of smoke, perfume, and sweat choking the air, when a wisp of a girl – she couldn't have been more than 18 -- came up to the stage. She was wearing a red dress that skimmed her body just right.

A curtain of black hair shimmered down to her waist, and her skin looked pale blue in the light. She tentatively took the mike and asked them to play in G, then launched into a bluesy version of "Mean to Me," an old Billie Holiday song.

By the middle of the second verse, people set their glasses down, stubbed out their cigarettes, and a hush fell over the room. Her voice was raw and unpolished but full of surprises. At first a sultry alto, she could hit the high notes in a silver soprano, then dip two octaves down to belt out the blues like a tenor. At first he thought it was a fluke – no one had that range and depth. He tested her, moving up the scale, changing the groove, even throwing her a sudden key change. She took it all with a serene smile, bobbing her head, eyes closed, adjusting perfectly. Her voice never wavered.

After a few numbers, the band took a break, and Jimmy Jay bought her a whiskey. As he passed her the drink, he noticed the contrast between her face, soft and round, and her eyes, dark and penetrating. Her name was Inez Youngblood, she said, and she'd just moved here from Tennessee. She was part Cherokee, once upon a time, but mostly mountain white.

"A hillbilly?" Jimmy Jay joked.

She threw him a dazzling smile that made his insides melt. "A hillbilly who sings the blues."

"Why Chicago?"

"I listen to the radio. Chicago blues is happy blues. You got Muddy Waters. Etta James. Chess Records. Everybody's here. Sweeping you up with their music. There just ain't no other place to sing." Those dark eyes bored into him. "And I got to sing."

By their third drink, he began to imagine the curves underneath that red dress, and what she looked like without it on. She had to know what he was thinking, because she smiled and started to finger a gold cross around her neck. Still, she didn't seem put off. More like she was teasing him.

Another set and half a reefer later, a fight broke out in the back of the bar. Inez, who was singing "Wang, Dang, Doodle" took it in stride, even when knives glinted and someone pulled out a piece. She just pointed to the fighters, asked the bartender to shine a spot in their direction, and leveled them with a hard look. The brawl moved into the alley. Jimmy Jay was impressed.

It was almost dawn when they quit playing. Someone bought a last round of drinks, and Jimmy Jay was just thinking about packing up when Inez came over.

"You're pretty damn good, Jimmy Jay."

He grinned. "Thanks, Hillbilly. You got a set of pipes yourself."

She laughed. "We ought to do this again."

Jimmy Jay suppressed his elation. "I could probably get us a couple of gigs."

She nodded. "I'd like that."

He nodded, just looking at her, not quite believing his good fortune.

She offered him a slow sensual smile. "Meanwhile, I got a favor to ask you, baby."

Jimmy Jay cleared his throat. "Yeah?" His voice cracked anyway.

She turned around, and lifted her hair off the back of her neck. "Help me take off my cross."

She ended up in his bed that night. And the next. And the night after that. She might only have been 18, but she was all heat and fire. All he had to do was touch her and she shivered with pleasure. When he ran his fingers slowly up her leg, starting at that perfectly shaped ankle, past her knee, stopping at the soft, pliant skin of her thigh, she would moan and grab him and pull him into her. Sliding underneath, rocking him hard, like she couldn't get enough.

"You are my sweet man," she would whisper when they stopped, exhausted and sweaty. "My sweet, sweet man."

They were a team for almost ten years. Inez, the hillbilly, soaring like an angel in one number, moaning like a whore in another; and Jimmy Jay, steadfast and sturdy, setting the beat, making her look good. Inez drove herself hard, and her sophistication grew. Her timing was impeccable. She rolled with the band, but could carry the show. If someone missed a chord, she covered them, and if they messed up their solo, she'd make light of it by singing scat, humming a chorus, or talking to the crowd.

Before long they were headlining at places like the Macomba before it burned down, South Side Johnny's, and Queenie's. Their only disagreement was over Chess Records and the two white owners who wanted to sign them. Jimmy Jay was all for it -- not only did his idol Willie Dixon work for Chess, but a record contract was something he'd dreamed about all his life. Inez kept saying they should hold out for a better deal. So far they had.

Even Calvin's arrival didn't slow them down. Calvin was a good baby who turned into a good boy. The same face and nappy hair as his Daddy; the high cheekbones and coffee-with-cream skin from his Mama. Inez seemed thrilled. She cooed and sang to him all day, but if Jimmy Jay figured she might retire, he figured wrong. Calvin came with them to the clubs on the South and West Sides, even to Peoria and East St. Louis. They'd bring blankets and put him to sleep in the back room on a ratty sofa, sometimes the floor. When he was older, Jimmy Jay or Inez would drop him off at school before they went to bed themselves. Jimmy Jay didn't mind. His own mama had brought him to all the blues joints.

Inez started calling them both her sweet men. Jimmy Jay would grin. They were happy. Real happy. Until the gig at Theresa's.

It was late autumn, and a chilly rain had been falling for two days, flooding the viaducts and lots of basements. Jimmy Jay and Inez were headlining at Theresa's Lounge on South Indiana. The place wasn't as upscale or as large as Macomba's, and the regulars, mostly people from the neighborhood, treated the place like home, dancing and talking with the players during the set. Tonight the smell of wet wool mixed with the smoke and booze and sweat.

A promoter from Capitol Records was in town and supposedly coming down that night. Inez was excited -- Capitol was huge, much bigger than Chess. Jimmy Jay was glad he'd talked a new lead guitar into playing the gig with them. Buddy Guy had just come up from Baton Rouge, and everyone was saying he was gonna change the face of the blues.

It was a knockout performance. No one missed a chord and the solos kicked. There were no amp or mike problems. Jimmy Jay and the drummer locked into a tight groove, and Buddy Guy's guitar was by turns brash, angry, and soulful. Inez's voice was as rich and mellow as thick honey. Even with the lousy weather, the place was packed, everyone swaying, dancing, bobbing their heads. It was like great sex, Jimmy Jay thought. Hot, sticky sex that trembled and throbbed and built, and ended in a long, fiery climax.

During the break, a white guy came up to the stage. He'd been at one of the back tables, smoking cigarettes. With his baby face and eager expression, he couldn't have been much older than Jimmy Jay. But his tailored suit and hair, slicked back with Bryl Crème, said he was trying to look well-off. He bought the band a round of drinks and nodded to Jimmy Jay. Then he turned to Inez and started talking quietly but earnestly. She looked from him to Jimmy Jay, then back at him. When she nodded, he took her hand and covered it with thick fingers. She didn't pull away. After the next set, Jimmy Jay caught them talking behind his back. By the last set, Inez was favoring him with the same smile she'd shot Jimmy Jay the first night at Macomba's ten years ago.

By the time Inez left town with him a week later, the rain had changed to snow. Jimmy Jay went to fetch Calvin at school. When he got back, she was gone. At first he thought she was at the store, picking up something for dinner, but when she didn't come home by six, an uneasy feeling swept over him. He checked the closet and drawers. Most of her things were gone. Except her gold cross.

Word got around that she'd run away with Billy Sykes. He hadn't worked for Capitol, it turned out. He did work in the record business, but dropped out of sight after he shorted some men who'd been financing a label with mob money. He reappeared a year later as a promoter. No one could say who his clients were.

That winter Jimmy Jay sat for hours on the bed, running Inez's gold cross and chain through his fingers. His mother moved in to look after Calvin who, at nine, was just old enough to realize his world had shattered. Word filtered back -- someone had seen her in Peoria, someone else heard she was in Iowa. Jimmy Jay tried to play, but he sounded tired and flat. Inez was inextricably bound up in his music and his life; with her gone, it felt like part of his body – worse, his soul -- had shriveled up and fallen off.

One day Calvin came in and saw him on the bed, fingering the cross with tears in his eyes.

"Don't be sad, Daddy." He came over and gave Jimmy Jay a hug. "I know what to do."

Jimmy Jay gazed at his son.

"Mama just got lost. She don't know how to get home. All we got to do is find her."

Jimmy Jay smiled sadly. "I don't think she wants to come home, boy."

"Granny says every mama wants to come home. All we needs do is find her. Once she sees us, it'll be just fine. I know it. "

Jimmy Jay tried to discourage him, but Calvin clung to his idea like a leech to a man's skin. He talked so much about finding his lost mama that after a while, his intensity infected Jimmy Jay. Could it really be that simple? Maybe Calvin was right. Sure Inez wanted to be a star, but she had a family. If they went after her, maybe she *would* realize what she'd given up and come home.

The following spring Billy Sykes brought Inez back to Chicago for a show on the West Side – no one on the South Side would book her. She was singing with some musicians from St. Louis, Jimmy Jay learned. They were staying at the Lincoln Hotel, a small, shabby place near the club.

Jimmy Jay waited until Calvin was home from school and had his supper. Then they both dressed in their Sunday best and took the bus to the hotel. Jimmy Jay slipped an old man at the desk a fiver and asked which room Inez Rollins was in. The man pointed up the steps. Jimmy Jay and Calvin climbed to the third floor and knocked on #315.

A tired female voice replied, "Yes?"

"It's me, Inez. And Calvin."

The door opened and suddenly Inez was there, her body framed in the light.

"Mama!" Calvin ran into her arms.

Her face lit, and she clasped Calvin so tight the boy could hardly suck in a breath. When she finally released him, she turned to Jimmy Jay.

"Hello, Jimmy Jay."

She looked washed-out, Jimmy Jay thought, although it gave him no pleasure to see it. Gaunt and nervous, too. Her eyes were rimmed in red, and her black mane of hair wasn't glossy. He thought he saw a bruise on her cheek, but she kept finger-combing her hair over the spot.

"Hello, Inez." He looked around. "Where's Sykes?"

"He's at the club. Getting ready for tonight."

Jimmy Jay nodded. He got right to the point. "We want you to come home. We are a family. Calvin needs you. So do I."

At least she had the decency to look ashamed. Her eyes filled. She gazed at Jimmy Jay, then Calvin. Then she shook her head.

"Why not?"

"Remember what I told you the first time we met?"

"You told me a lot of things."

"I need to sing, Jimmy Jay. And Billy's gonna make me a star."

Jimmy Jay saw the determination on her face, as raw as the first time he'd met her. His heart cracked, but he struggled to conceal his grief. _He_ might have lost her, but Calvin didn't have to. "Take the boy. He needs his mama. I'll – I'll pay you for him, 'ifin you want."

"I'll think about it." Inez looked down at Calvin, trailed her fingers through his hair, and smiled. Calvin snuggled closer. "I'll talk to Billy when he gets back."

Jimmy Jay nodded. "I'll leave the boy with you. I'll pick him up at the club when you start your gig. We can talk more."

Inez looked sad but grateful. Calvin looked thrilled.

Two hours later, the band had finished setting up but there was no sign of Inez. Or Billy Sykes. Or Calvin. Jimmy Jay saw the uneasiness on the musicians' faces, heard one of them say, "Where are those damn fools?"

He retraced his steps to the Lincoln Hotel.

No one was behind the desk when Jimmy Jay got there. He went up the stairs and down the hall. Music blared out from Inez's room. The radio. Benny Goodman's orchestra, he thought. He was about to knock on the door when he saw something move at the other end of the hall. Something small. He wheeled around and squinted.

"Calvin? Is that you?"

The figure trotted toward him. Calvin, looking small and lonely.

"What you doin' out here, son? Where's your mama?"

Calvin didn't say anything, just shrugged.

"Is she inside?" Jimmy Jay pointed to the door.

Calvin nodded.

"Is Sykes back?"

Calvin nodded again.

Jimmy Jay turned back to the door, leaned his ear against it. The music was loud. He knocked. No one answered. Probably couldn't hear him above the music. He knocked again, and when no one responded, started to push against the door.

"Inez, Sykes…. Open up!"

Nothing. Except the music.

Jimmy Jay looked both ways down the hall, then threw his weight against the door. It almost gave. He backed up, turned sideways, and rammed himself against it again. This time the door gave, and Jimmy Jay burst into the room.

He was still holding the gun when the police arrived. Inez's body was at the foot of the bed, but Sykes' was halfway to the door. A pool of blood was congealing under each of them.

### 1982: Chicago

Three weeks later, Jimmy Jay no longer had the strength to get out of bed. Calvin was putting in twelve-hour days. He knew it was an excuse for not dealing with his father, but he couldn't bear to come home to a place where death hovered in the air.

One night, though, was different. As he trudged inside, Calvin heard music from upstairs. And laughter. When he climbed the steps, he saw that Jeanine had moved their stereo into Jimmy Jay's room. An old album revolved on the turntable. His father was in bed, eyes closed, snapping his fingers. Jeanine was sitting in the chair smiling too, her head bobbing to the music. Calvin peered at the album cover. Chess Records. Muddy Waters.

His father opened his eyes. "Hey, Calvin." His face was wreathed in smiles. "There ain't nothing like Muddy for an old soul. With Willie Dixon and Howlin' Wolf on backup. Lord, it makes me see the gates of heaven."

"Don't talk that way, Dad."

Jimmy Jay dismissed him with a wave of his hand. When the song came to an end, Calvin lifted the needle and turned off the stereo. Jeanine went downstairs, claiming dishes that needed to be washed.

"Calvin," his father said, "We can't put it off no more. It's time to talk about the arrangements."

Calvin stiffened. He dug in his pocket for his Luckys, pulled one out and lit it. He sat in the chair. "I don't know why you want to be buried there."

His father eyed him. "She was my wife, Calvin. And your mama."

"She was white trash!" Calvin exhaled a cloud of white smoke. "White trailer trash."

"Don't you ever talk that way 'bout your mama!" His father's voice was unexpectedly strong. "And she was from the mountains of Tennessee, boy," his father added. "The Smoky Mountains."

But Calvin wasn't mollified. "She ran out on us. You and me. She left us. And for what?"

His father just looked at him. Then he turned his head toward the window. "She was my woman," he said quietly, his burst of energy now dissipated. "And I was her sweet man."

Calvin felt his stomach pitch. The black hole was opening up again, and all he wanted to do was jump in and let it consume him. He stubbed out his cigarette, letting the window fan clear the smoke. Jeanine ran it all the time, even though it didn't do much cooling. Beads of sweat popped out on his forehead .

"I still miss her, son."

Calvin swallowed. "Pop, don't."

"I ain't got no regrets." His father said. "And now, in a little while, if the good Lord is willin', I'll see her again."

Calvin's throat got hot. He felt tears gather at the back of his eyes. He tried to blink them away, hoping his father wouldn't notice. But he did.

"Why you crying, Calvin? You're a good son. And Jeanine is a good woman. She been taking good care of me."

"It's not that." The words spilled out.

His father cocked his head. The slight movement seemed to require more energy than he could muster.

"I – I got to tell you something."

His father's body might be wasted, but his soul seemed to expand. His eyes grew huge, taking over his entire face. "What's that, son?"

The black hole widened. Calvin had to take the plunge. "That – that night…" Calvin's words were heavy and sluggish, as if the hole was already sucking him down. "The night mama died …." Calvin whispered. "It was my fault. I killed Mama."

An odd look registered on Jimmy Jay's face.

"After you left …" Calvin's voice was flat and hard."… Mama sang to me. And hugged me. It felt – so good… So right."

"Your mama had the voice of an angel."

Calvin held his hand up to stop him. "Then Billy Sykes come back. He was pissed when he saw me. 'What's that kid doing here?' He yelled. He and Mama -- well, she told him she wanted to take me with them. Sykes wouldn't have none of it. 'Are you crazy?' He said. 'It's bad enough that you're a hillbilly. And part Injun. I ain't taking your colored kid, too. Get rid of him.'

"Mama begged him. 'He won't be no trouble,' she kept saying and looked at me. 'Will you, sweet man?'

"But Sykes kept saying no. 'I put too much of my money in you to throw it away. What are people gonna think when they see you with a colored kid?'

"Mama and me were on the bed. She was hugging me real tight. 'I want my son,' she said.

"'He'll be in the way,' Sykes said. 'You want to be a star? You got to make a choice. Me or the kid.'"

Jimmy Jay didn't say anything.

Calvin shuddered. "Mama said, 'Don't make me do that. I'm his Mama!'"

"'Then I'll make the choice for you.' Sykes said. And he pulls out a gun and aims it at my head." Calvin looked at the floor.

"What happened then, son?" Jimmy Jay asked, his voice almost as flat as Calvin's.

Calvin covered his eyes with his hand. "Mama got up from the bed. She looked scared. 'All right. All right. Put that gun away, Billy. I'll send Calvin back to his Daddy. Just put the gun away. Before someone gets hurt.' Then she looked from me to Sykes. She didn't say nothing more."

Calvin pressed his lips together. He couldn't look at his father, but he knew his father was staring at him.

"Sykes started to put the gun away, but then -- I don't know, Pop -- something came over me. I jumped up and tackled Sykes. Right there in the room." He hesitated. "The gun went off. And Mama dropped off the end of the bed. Just dropped dead right in front of me."

His father whispered, "And then?"

"Sykes was like a crazy man. It was like he couldn't believe what happened. He started screaming, first at mama. Kept telling her to get up and stop foolin' around. But she didn't, Pop. She never got up." Calvin's voice cracked. "Then he dropped the gun and started for the door. He was gonna take off! Just leave her there." Calvin paused again. "I just couldn't let that happen. I couldn't. When he was halfway to the door, I picked up the gun and shot him in the back."

Calvin felt tears streaming down his face.

Jimmy Jay, his eyes veiled, let out a quiet breath. Calvin heard the hum of traffic through the window above the fan.

After a long time, Calvin said haltingly, "I guess it's time to go to the police."

"You won't do nothing of the kind, son." His father raised himself on one elbow. "I already done the time. For both of us. And..." His features softened. "...I figured out what happened a long time ago."

"You knew?" Calvin's stomach turned over. "How?"

"There was no way your mama could do anything to hurt you. Or you her. I knew it had to be an accident. At least with her. And Sykes... well..." Jimmy Jay shrugged as if it didn't matter.

"You knew? All these years?" Calvin felt his features contort with anguish. "I killed them, and you took the rap for me?"

Jimmy Jay nodded. "And I'd do it all over again."

Calvin searched his father's face for an explanation. The silence pressed in.

"You were just a boy," Jimmy Jay finally said, gazing at him with an expression of infinite sadness, compassion, and love. "I done the time for you both...so you would grow up and turn into her sweet man. Now..." He paused. "We got to get back to that plannin.' The Lord 'll be givin' Inez back her other sweet man, and I need to be ready. We still got a lot of music to make together."

## Sara Peak Convery

As the shift from film to digital was starting, I used my remaining stash of b/w film. I photographed several women with emotionally significant articles of clothing. "Judith's Back" (2010) was one of several artworks I made using these images. Judith, an actress , had a dress belonging to a very dignified woman who was something of an anomaly in her family.

I interviewed a group of women for my Grass Widow Sod Widow project, starting in 2008. An old phrase rarely used, a grass widow is a divorced or estranged woman (*cut the grass*) and a sod widow has buried her spouse (*dig up the sod*). After conducting many interviews I realized that I needed other images for the stories of these women. "Bedtime"(2011) was from a honeymoon snapshot of one of the grass widows. She divorced her husband 25 years later. The image to me is a sort of death fortold.

After I moved to my new studio space in 2019, I finally had space to assess what materials I had on hand. Over the years I had acquired a number of abandoned canvases, left at art centers where I had taken classes in order to have a space to work.  I put out a call on Facebook to friends: "give me an assignment!" A fellow artist suggested "paint the home you grew up in from memory." This was one of the few times that I had tried to paint without a visual reference. I chose a pair of abandoned portraits and covered them with translucent magenta paint. "My Uncle's Trunk and Other Bedroom Stories" (diptych, 2019) is evocative for its color scheme but also the sense of something hidden that you can never really see.

"My Fear Makes You Dangerous" (2020) As the Orange Menace stoked the shift to the right, I made flags.  Some with overt messages, others with hidden words. Titling and word choice were and continue to be a challenge. Leading up to the 2020 election, this seemed more and more important.

*My Fear Makes You Dangerous*

*Judith's Back*

*Bedtime*

*My Uncle's Trunk and Other Bedroom Stories*

Tim Chapman

## *Secret Garden*

The woods were foreign to Ben. The uneven ground upset his balance, and as he ran he caught his boots on roots and rocks, stumbling, getting up and stumbling again. Branches whipped across his face, stinging, blinding him. He had left the path to elude the two teenage boys who were chasing him, but he was making too much noise. He paused a moment to rest, his back against a tall tree, and listened. A cloud of mosquitoes found him, but over the hum he could hear the boys shouting to one another as they ran, one of them calling his name and whooping. "Ben! C'mon, old man, whooo! We got ya!"

They were close, Ben thought, and they'd split up, trying to flank him. He ran on, moving away from the shouting. He wiped his face with the grimy sleeve of his pea coat and panicked when he saw the red, his face bleeding from a half dozen small cuts.

"Yo, Ben!" One of them was on his left. He could see movement through the foliage, something blue behind all the green. He cut right, zigzagging now in an effort to keep the trees between himself and his pursuer. Suddenly the branches parted, and he was in a small clearing. He didn't like being out in the open, but he couldn't turn back. He stooped low and moved off to his right, wading through the tall grass, hoping to double back and find some place to hide. A rock turned under his foot and he fell, catching himself on hands and knees. When he looked up he saw one of the boys standing in the middle of the clearing, whistling and waving at someone behind him. Ben turned and saw the other boy, the one who had shouted, emerge from the woods, smiling and fitting a hunting bolt onto the flight rail of a crossbow. Ben stood and faced the boy, holding his arms out, pleading. An arrow flew from behind and pierced his right forearm. Ben screamed. He turned toward the boy who had shot him and saw him place the end of his crossbow on the ground, put his foot into the metal stirrup and bend to grip the string. Ben started to run until another arrow chunked into his thigh. This time he went down hard, pushed himself to his knees and started to crawl. Through the roaring in his ears he heard the click of the first boy's cocking mechanism as he pulled the bowstring into place. The boys took turns, one fired while the other loaded and so on. They kept firing long after Ben was dead.

Music blared from the car radio as Mary inched through traffic, but she wasn't really listening. She was thinking about the walls of her cubicle. They were the color of cream of broccoli soup. Depressing. She would probably have canned soup for lunch, but the question was where—desk or diner? She hated eating at her desk, and it only took a few minutes to drive to the diner. The diner soup tasted like it was canned too. Probably came from a fifty-five gallon drum.

She was thinking about soup when smoke began streaming from under the hood of her car. She pulled onto the shoulder and switched off the engine. The smoke was thick, and it was swirling around the car like cream poured into a glass of iced coffee. She took her suit coat and purse and walked up the embankment to watch it. The smell of burning plastic reminded her of the new carpet fumes at her office. Both odors nauseated her. She considered the possibility that the car might explode, like on TV, and she thought that would be cool. She wasn't even upset. She didn't care if she got to work or not. She looked around and saw an oak near a clump of bushes, walked over and sat in the shade under the tree. In fact, she didn't care if she ever got to work. "Why bother," she said out loud. "I sell crap to people so I can make enough money to buy the crap someone else is trying to sell to me. The company can easily swap me out for some other widget."

She took out her cell phone, and called her husband.

"Jeffrey, my car's on fire."

"Holy shit!" he said. "Are you okay?"

"Better than okay," she said. "I've had a revelation."

Just then the gas tank ruptured. There was no explosion, but the spreading gasoline caught fire, and flames shot up into the morning sky. The car was engulfed in black smoke.

She couldn't explain why she wasn't coming home, and having to come up with a reason frustrated her, so she threw her phone into the burning car. He must have tried to call her back because she could hear her ringtone for a minute before the phone melted. She smiled, thinking about how irritated Jeffrey must be. He was a man for whom everything had come easily. Tall, with great hair and a prominent jaw line, his ascent from copywriter to managing director to vice president had been swift and sure. She could have made creative director, they worked at the same company, but after they married she realized that working for her husband would kill the marriage, so she went to another firm. Jeffrey was annoyingly smug in his effortless success, but Jeffrey wasn't the problem. She didn't want to go to work, and she didn't want to go home, and she didn't know why. Then she remembered the grocery store.

There's a TV in the checkout line that plays commercials for products the store sells. One day last week, she had gotten in line and the TV was showing a commercial for cereal. She watched it for a second, then left the line and went to the cereal aisle. When she got back in line there was a commercial for baked beans playing. She turned around and, even though she doesn't like baked beans, went to get some. After she paid, the clerk handed her some coupons for other products she might want to purchase. The coupons had been selected by a computer based on her previous buying habits. I don't want a computer analyzing my purchases, she thought, and I certainly don't want to watch commercials on screens above checkout lines or gas pumps or read the framed ads in the stalls of public washrooms. I don't want to be told how to dress or what to buy or that I'm too fat or too old. I don't want to be a consumer.

She started with a little tent in the bushes, but soon she had to move further into the woods. People could see her camp from the highway, and one morning she saw a cop car pull onto the shoulder.

Jeffrey really is being very good about the whole thing, she thought. The girls were pretty much on their own, the youngest away at college, and Jeffrey spent most of their time together glued to the television. With the kids gone they didn't have a lot to talk about, and sex had become a perfunctory activity for them. Being post-menopausal was a liberating experience for her, but she knew that her lack of interest was difficult for Jeffrey. She used to wish he would find a mistress until it dawned on her that television had become his mistress. His ad sense would kick in during the commercials, and he often critiqued them out loud.

For a while Jeffrey came to see her every day, then once a week, then less. And he always brought soup, as though each can contained his apology for a marriage that had run its course. The last time she saw him he gave her two cases of corn chowder.

"You'll like this. It's a thick soup with a nice texture, southwestern style, so there's a little zing to it."

"Thanks," she said.

He stood there, holding the case of soup, looking for a place to set it down. "Some reporters came by. They heard about you and wanted to know why you were living out here."

"Did you tell them?" she asked.

"How could I," he said. "I don't understand it, either."

He set the soup down and went back to his car for the second case. Mary opened the first box and pulled out a can. It was a more expensive soup than the others he had brought. Jeffrey wasn't cheap, exactly, but he wasn't the sort of person to splurge on soup. This was his way of cleansing his conscience. Mary knew he wouldn't be back.

Colin unscrewed the barbed head of the crossbow bolt, pushed the shaft back out of the hole in the man's neck, and tossed the two parts into an open backpack. He paused to watch his friend struggling with the one in the man's calf.

"This thing is stuck tight, must've hit bone."

"Try pushing it all the way through, Dick." He handed him a large, flat-faced rock. "You can borrow my hammer."

The two sat in the middle of a clearing surrounded by woods on three sides and a river on the fourth. Unlike their dark-haired victim, both were blond. They wore baggy, madras plaid shorts and 'crombie t-shirts. Dick was over six feet tall and gangly and felt uncomfortable sitting on the ground. He showed it by continually slapping imaginary insects off his legs. "Did you get our hundred dollar bill back?" he asked.

"It was in his coat pocket along with his VA card and some other junk. You'd think these old bums would be a bit more cautious about why some stranger wants to give them a hundred bucks. Hell, between the homeless alkies and the day laborers standing on street corners looking for work, we've practically got an endless supply."

"Yeah. The city's full of suckers." Dick looked around the clearing. A shallow grave waited next to the corpse, and mounds of overturned earth marked the three graves containing their previous victims. "Hey, why do we have to take the bolts with us, anyway? We should just bury these human pincushions the way they are. Besides, this is taking too long. It's giving me the creeps."

"Relax," Colin said. "We're fine. No one ever comes out here. And we have to take the bolts because, if the bodies are found, we don't want the cops looking for guys with crossbows. Without these bolts our chubby friend here could just as easily have been shot with a regular arrow from a bow. Besides, they're expensive." He crawled over to the grave and shoveled a little more dirt out with his entrenching tool. "Looks like he's going to need more room. That was a nice shot, by the way."

"What, through the calf? Thanks." He chuckled. "Dude went down like a water buffalo."

"That reminds me," Colin said, "you ever have a heel spur?"

"What? Hell, no. What is it?"

"It's a pain, starts in your heel and moves up your leg. I think I got it from track practice. I could barely keep up with this lard ass today."

Dick gave the bolt another whack with the rock and the barbed head popped out of the corpse's shin. "Ah, that got it. Nope, never had a heel spur. What do you take for it?" He sat back and set his feet on the corpse's hip and shoulder, then shoved him into the grave. Colin started to cover him with dirt.

"I dunno," he said, "but I've got to find something. It's fuckin' killing me."

They gathered up their crossbows and backpacks and started the long hike back through the woods. Colin winced with each limping step.

Mary gave up the tent when the people showed up. By that time Maize had come to stay with her. Maize was the biggest cat she'd ever seen, brown with white patches and missing part of his tail and part of an ear, and the only cat she'd ever known who liked corn chowder. That's why she named him Maize. Like the Indian word, she thought. Maize wouldn't let Mary pet him, but at night he slept pressed against her back for warmth.

Mary liked the way he felt, all firm and muscly but kind of soft at the same time. They moved to a spot behind an abandoned factory when the crowds got too thick. Most of them were people who had heard about her on TV. Some were homeless or had lost their jobs. Some had substance abuse problems or were just plain nuts, but some were dropouts, like her. They just started showing up, setting up their tents and making a lot of noise. Some of them tried to make friends, but Mary wasn't interested. The last time she counted, there were over a hundred of them, and they just kept coming. Someone nicknamed her "Lady Luddite," a name that thrilled the news media. A local television reporter cajoled her into an interview. She tried to explain that she had nothing against technology per se; what she objected to was the way it was being used to turn human beings into commodities. The reporter ended the interview with, "And there you have it. Words of wisdom from the woman who hates society, Lady Luddite."

She gave a woman with a little girl her tent before she left. The girl called Maize "Kitkit" and kept trying to pick him up. "Why the hell would you let your daughter play with a feral cat?" Mary asked the woman. "The kid's lucky Maize didn't take her eye out." She and Maize were both glad to leave.

They set up housekeeping in a lean-to made of wood pallets covered with plastic. She stacked them against the back wall of an abandoned factory for support. There was a big, overgrown field behind the factory where the railroad tracks and the loading platforms used to be. The walls were covered with gang graffiti, but she wasn't worried. Gangs didn't care about crazy cat ladies. On the other side of the field was a forest preserve.

It was Maize who helped her learn to hunt and forage. One day Mary found a dead rodent in front of the lean-to. She thought it was a vole. It looked kind of like a mouse, but its eyes were small for its face and it had a pointier nose. It would have been beautiful except for its long claws. Maize had killed it and brought it home. Mary stroked the little animal with her thumb, admiring its soft, velvety fur, then stashed it under an overturned pot. That night she skinned it and added it to some tomato soup to make a little vole stew. She had long ago run out of corn chowder.

After that she spent a good part of every day roaming the forest preserve, collecting edible plants and filling jugs with water from the little river that bisected the preserve. She quickly learned to boil the water before drinking it, and she only ate plants she knew were non-poisonous. Even then, the taste took some getting used to. Some days she wouldn't find much of anything, but she never worried. She loved foraging, and she loved swimming. She had spent most of her teenage summers at her family's lakefront, Wisconsin cabin. Her parents would probably have said she was an introvert, but she liked to think of herself as independent. She would leave the cabin early, before anyone was up, and march into the woods with a swimsuit, towel, and a few sandwiches in a bag, not returning until dinnertime. Her explorations involved climbing trees, hiking off-trail, wading through streams, and swimming in the lake. She collected milkweed pods with their fluffy contents bursting out and cast off cicada shells, awed that the split skin retained all the detail of the insect. One summer she found a secluded meadow with a pixie ring, a circle of mushrooms, growing in it.

This quickly became her favorite spot, and she would spend hours there, daydreaming and singing made-up songs. She thought of it as her secret garden.

Thirty-five years later, her body was remembering. She shed layers of fat and her skin quickly colored under the late-summer sun. Her hair, no longer dyed, was streaked with grey, and it rippled as she sliced through the water, flowing dolphin-like, her cupped hands pulling her forward. Now, her explorations had purpose. She collected cattail shoots and water lilies. She hunted frogs at dusk and snuck up on turtles sunning themselves at midday. At first her catch was small, but soon she learned how to lead them, anticipating timing and direction. The frogs tasted better, but the turtles were easier to catch. Most turtles dived straight down before making the run to the dark water under the riverbank's overhang.

She was lounging in the late afternoon sun on a mossy patch of riverbank after a day of fishing. She was drunk on the musty smell of the river mixed with the pine of the surrounding trees, and she opened her lungs to suck in the air. Her pronged gigging stick and a mesh bag with her catch, two large turtles and half a dozen bluegill, lay nearby. Maize slept at her feet. Who knew cats could snore, she thought. A cool breeze raised a few goose bumps on her bare skin, making her aware of her body. Her flat stomach and muscled thighs amazed her. At fifty, she was in the best shape of her life. She started to think of all the diets she'd tried, but stopped. Thinking about her civilized self made her melancholy. She had no desire to go back, but she missed her children. "They must think I'm crazy," she said. Then she remembered the last time they had all been together, Jeffrey watching television and the girls constantly texting their friends; all of them together but not together. She wished she could explain her self-imposed exile to them, but she knew they wouldn't understand. They were glad participants in a system that cared more about their pocketbooks than their humanity.

Maize heard the noise first. Instantly awake, his ears turned toward the sound, and he shifted his weight onto his haunches, ready to run. Mary moved behind a tree and pulled on her shorts, t-shirt and sneakers. People were coming toward them, running through the woods and shouting. Mary considered climbing a tree to get a look at them but rejected the idea. She didn't want to be stuck in a tree if they spotted her. She grabbed her catch bag and bent low, moving along the riverbank until she found a mound of dirt covered with prairie grass. She lay on her stomach and inched forward through the grass to get a view of the clearing. She hissed at Maize to follow her, but the cat stayed where he was.

Someone emerged from the woods across the clearing, just opposite Mary's hiding place. A man, she thought, and he carried something that looked like a short rifle. He knelt beside a log at the edge of the clearing and raised the rifle to his shoulder. Another man came into the clearing about twenty feet to the left of the first man. This one ran hunched over, holding his stomach. A third man stepped into the clearing on the same path as the running man. He carried a short rifle, too. The running man was coming toward her when he suddenly stood, arching his body as though something had struck him in the back and then pitched forward to disappear into the tall grass. The wind rippled the grass in her direction, like waves on an ocean, carrying with it the sound of the fallen man's crying.

At first she thought the man had tripped. There had been no shot, no report from the rifles. The two standing men walked to where the other man lay, and she could see that they were no older than her youngest daughter. They pointed their rifles down. This time Mary heard the twang of the bowstrings, and the fallen man stopped crying. She pressed her forehead into the dirt and closed her eyes. Civilization had found her, and it had brought murder with it.

She backed down the way she had come and was about to cross the river to the woods on the other side when she saw Maize, standing in a crouch, his ears flat against his head and one of the men moving toward him, fitting an arrow into his crossbow.

"Hey Colin," the man shouted over his shoulder, "I'll bet you five bucks I can get this cat with one shot."

"Leave it alone, Dick," Colin said, "and help me bury this guy. He smells like beer and piss."

Dick ignored him and lay on his stomach, adjusting the telescopic sight on his crossbow as he aimed at Maize. Mary started to panic. She hissed at the cat, but he ignored her. She picked up a rock with the intention of spoiling the man's shot but realized that he was too far away. She didn't trust her aim. In frustration, she stood and threw the rock at Maize. The cat was so wound up that he leaped into the air, then ran up the nearest tree. Dick tried to get a bead on him, but he was used to larger targets. The arrow thunked harmlessly into the base of the tree.

Mary tried to duck back into the tall grass, but it was too late. Dick had spotted her, and he was scared. "Colin!" he shouted. "We've got a witness—a goddamned witness!"

Mary watched, unable to move, as Dick cocked the crossbow, putting his foot in the stirrup and pulling back the string. She wanted to run, to get across the river, but she had seen the speed and power of the arrow he fired at Maize. She imagined being hit as she swam, her blood swirling, mixing with the water, the current piloting her lifeless body downstream. The string clicked into place, and Dick reached to pull an arrow from the quiver on his belt. Mary started to run. She didn't run away but ran straight at him, screaming, a forest banshee trailing the mesh bag behind her. The sight startled him, slowing him just long enough for Mary to reach him. Before Dick could load his weapon she was in front of him, swinging the mesh bag up from the ground with all the power of her anger and fear. The bag split open as the turtles cracked him on the side of his head, and he fell back, the arrow slipping from his fingers. He looked up at her from his seat among the spilled fish.

"You crazy bitch!" he shouted. A red welt was growing over his eye, and he rubbed it, then reached for the fallen arrow. Mary snatched it up and took a step back. She would have run then, but she saw Colin level his crossbow, aiming at her head. "Stay down!" Colin shouted, but Dick ignored him and sprang to his feet, reaching for her just as his friend fired. The arrow slammed into the base of his skull, throwing him forward to clutch at Mary as he fell past her. She stood, staring down at the dying boy until she heard Colin scream. It was a long, sorrowful wail, garbled and unintelligible, but she understood it's meaning as he stumbled toward her, and the cry morphed from pain to rage. Colin raised his crossbow over his head, wielding it like a club, and Mary leapt to meet him. She struck at him with the arrow in her hand, forgetting its lethality, piercing his neck, severing his carotid artery. Without meaning to, she killed the boy.

Autumn came quickly to the forest. Mary had spent most of one day hiking to the nearest gas station. The attendant let her use his cell phone, their pay phone having been taken out years before. She called Jeffrey, and when he didn't answer she sent him a text message—Bring warm clothes and soup please :-) She added the smiley-face emoji on a whim. Jeffrey brought her a carload of supplies and worried letters from their daughters, imploring her to come home. Instead, she and Maize abandoned the pallet lean-to and moved deeper into the woods. She kept Colin's entrenching tool after using it to bury the two boys in the clearing, and she used it to dig a wide pit over which she constructed a dome of branches and vinyl-coated, nylon tarps. She left a hole in the center, like the ones she had seen in yurts and teepees, which she could open or close for ventilation, allowing her to have small, indoor fires on cold nights.

She had buried the boys so that their graves, along with the graves of their victims, formed a circle, and she visited the clearing at least once a week. She didn't mourn the boys, though she felt bad for the men they had killed. She went there because it was a peaceful place. Sometimes she would sit silently, watching Maize stalk field mice in the tall grass, and sometimes she would nap in the afternoon sun. She often thought of it as a holy place. In the winter she came just to marvel at the way the shadows curved and stretched across the snow-covered mounds, and in the spring she planted choruses of wildflowers on the graves.

# Rachel L. Robbins

I teach art, creative writing, and composition in a community college where students claim they don't "get" poetry. Then they turn up the volume on their headphones and bob their heads to music and mouth the words. Poetry is inherent and intuitive for all of us. The rules can be evasive. Formlessness itself becomes a form. I often find myself trying to pinpoint what I love so much about poetry. There is something about the silences between words, the inhale interrupting the tempo of the slam poet, the anticipation as we turn the page. Sometimes, by saying something that means nothing at all, we are much closer to saying something. I spent many years studying this and attempting to understand the phenomenon. And then I had a baby. When I read to my daughter at night about brown bears and herring fish stars, I tap into that same elusive world. She looks at the page and she looks up at me, and she understands without understanding the words.

My debut book of poetry, "In Lieu of Flowers," was dubbed a collage in book form for the way it transmuted narrative and abstraction through text, painting, and fabric collage. Painting was always an essential part of my process, and then the balance began to teeter. My writing took a back seat to colors and forms. I began spending whole summers exploring my poems and stories as large scale murals sprawling across walls in the city. Time and again I was hired to paint nurseries and design work for children that were afraid of the dark. I began experimenting with glow-in-the-dark paint, but it wasn't until I became pregnant and had my own daughter that the horizon of the nursery illuminated with possibilities. I filled the skyline of her walls with birch trees and owls, jungles and stars. Everything I paint, I paint for her.

## The Blood in the Veins

Let's Call This Place Shangri-la

The Musician

Jennifer Worrell

## *Cross Your Fingers*

"Now wait 'til I tell you about Cambodia…"

Wayne's boss, Marie, droned on while Judy sipped her wine.

*Gulped. Be honest, Judy.*

Wayne leaned forward, chin in hand, eyes sparkling like the silver he insisted Judy polish for dinner. Fresh off the plane after her tour of Asia, Marie deserved a fine meal since she had graciously gone on this trip in his place. It wasn't his fault the baby arrived early, Marie insisted. It simply couldn't be helped. Decked out in a pristine white suit of Japanese silk, red Chinese slippers, and filigree earrings from who-knows-where, she regaled them with whirlwind adventures, still high on the adrenaline of nonstop meetings and flights, still flushed from tight schedules and the poshest hotels.

Wayne Junior slept—soundly, for the first time—wrapped in the bamboo blanket that Wayne Senior might have bought himself. But he didn't see Marie's gift as a slight. He saw nothing but the luster of success. Smelled it in the form of sweet jasmine. Leaned into it when he shook Marie's hand goodbye, as though trying to squeeze prosperity from her fingers.

He walked her to her cab, somehow turning it into a twenty-minute journey. Extreme fatigue and a headache materialized the second he stepped back over the threshold. Judy bounced Junior on her hip, his father's absence having stabbed a hole in his placid baby dreams, and smiled through the squall.

"Yes honey," she said, "a lie-down will do you good."

*You bastard.*

A second honeymoon in Thailand was Judy's idea. The one country Marie hadn't visited. The trip itself was Judy's mother's idea, pitched in a flurry of fits and starts and side-eye glances. She was overjoyed to take the baby, she'd said. Couldn't wait to spoil him as only a grandmother could. Wayne retreated into his travel books and business dinners and late-night, closed-door phone calls as though he hadn't heard.

While Wayne tied up loose ends in the hotel's business center, Judy spent the first three days hiking through Pattaya. From a quiet hilltop, a temple with sweeping curves and intricate spires reached above the trees into the clouds. Judy climbed down for a closer look.

Every inch of the temple's imposing stature carved from solid teak, it reminded her of the Cambodian architecture they had scrolled through for hours, hunched over Marie's phone. Even here, she followed.

Hundreds of hands, decades of sweat and toil, and the entire thing would one day collapse into a pile of sticks and dust, no matter what anyone did to bolster it. 'Sanctuary of Truth,' the visitor's sign read. *How fitting.*

Someone grabbed Judy around the waist. She wrenched in their grip, throwing weak punches until she recognized his face.

*How could I forget the way this felt?*

"Expecting someone else?" he teased, without the silver sparkle. *Only wooden structures here.*

"You didn't have to come so soon, I know you're busy."

"You said 'if I wanted.' I'm free."

"You sure?"

He stared up at the ornate archway, followed the labyrinth of dragons' tails and twisting vines across the ceiling and back towards the entrance. "Of course. Nowhere else I'd be."

Molia Dumbleton

## *What Real Men Wish They Dreamed*

On the day his buddy blew his hand off on a sack of premature ANFO, The Miner wrapped the frizzled hand in his favorite flannel shirt and set it next to him on the bench-seat of his truck while his buddy sat passenger, bleeding more than he'd ever seen someone bleed and howling like he'd only ever heard from dogs. The nurses didn't bring the hand back after he handed it to them in the ER, which meant The Miner hadn't seen his shirt again neither, and he was rattling with cold by the time they drugged his buddy into dumb silence and told The Miner to go home and wash up, rest. At home he sat on the couch and shook so hard his dog wouldn't even sit with him.

When The Miner finally felt sleep coming from far off, he leaned over onto the scratchy cushions and tried to hook it, gentle but steady, and tug it to him like a fish on a line. He made a wish for what he would like to dream: Not of coal or blood, or gold, or even his now-gone shirt, which he had liked to ball up under his head for sleeping, and which he missed now. But of his dead mother, who whenever he had gotten a hole, used to darn it right on his foot while he was still wearing it. Tickling his toes with her rounded needle-eye and winking at him, tease-scolding *Don't you dare wiggle, now.*

Molia Dumbleton

# *Why Shit Is Still Like This Around Here and Probably Always Will Be*

Joey says his crispest memory of his mom is that ticky-ticky click-click-click of high heels on linoleum in the mornings and the clatter of plastic dishes and bracelets and curse words in the sink and her insistence that he hug her low and fast before she put on her pantyhose *Jesus c'mon hurry now be a good boy* because they're expensive and runs were always blamed on him *Goddamnit Joey* even when he didn't touch her legs not at all and all his trucks were in the other room besides.

The sound of those wind chimes she hung on the front porch still gets to him now he swears they put him in some kinda mood real fast whenever some girl he's trying to go home with has them outside her apartment when they get there *For fuck's sake chimes you gotta be kidding me* rubbing his nose in the way her sweet smoky smell used to go out the door with her into the cold air and into that loud car of hers down the road and away again an entire heart's lifetime tick-ticking away in his chest before Mrs. Lewin and her big smell would get there to find him alone truck-handed and gob-faced at the plastic glass of the storm front door.

Molia Dumbleton

# *The During (12 hrs, 40 min)*

They hadn't spoken since Minnesota. They'd even gassed up, restroomed, and resupplied in Beloit without a word, surprised to find old signals still at their fingertips, even after the eleven years of divorce that had followed their nineteen years of marriage.

They were headed to Ohio, to their twin daughters' college graduation, and an empty trailer clattered behind them. It was grating, but June supposed it made the silence between them less noticeable.

Still on the outskirts of Minneapolis, she had said something about road construction and Bill had nodded slowly, with a level of attention that seemed excessive. It was the way they had been taught to listen in marriage therapy: to lean the body forward, tilt the head, lower the brow. An acrobatic checklist. But its purpose, they had also been told, was to indicate, beyond risk of misinterpretation, that the listener understood and appreciated what the speaker was saying.

Or, June surmised, to indicate that the listener did not want to part, after all.

She spent a great deal of Wisconsin speculating that if this kind of listening were to occur years *after* the parting, it might mean something else entirely. Perhaps that the listener had taken note of the new life that had peeked out of the speaker *since* the parting. Perhaps a life that hadn't been noticed *before* the parting, or that maybe even hadn't been there yet. Or, perhaps, that *had* been there in the beginning, but had been siphoned away in the during. In the child-rearing and overworking and the constancy of duty. But that, in any case, surely had *not* been there anymore in the end, when a cold fog had blown in and laid damp over the conversations and the bedroom, and turned their eyes flat upon one another.

Still, June had taken note of this forward lean, and spent most of Illinois warming to the idea of relaxing that now-worn muscle. Of, having crossed dangerous terrain, finally setting tired feet back across safe border.

She could see it like a diagram now: two vectors shooting outward in separate directions, with all the logic of bottle rockets. Spiraling, smoking, into loves and fitness clubs, new pets, glass-walled lofts, classes at the college. A flourishing. Years passing. A sheen upon both of them as they took turns gaining and losing weight, smugly recommending new bands, and showing up late to things, rosy from having just stepped from other people's beds. They had improved themselves to the point of boredom and finally found the blame in themselves for whatever that thing was that had once been missing.

It was hard to remember what it had been. She had overworked; she didn't anymore. He had kept score, tabulating the ways she was neglecting him while she rattled from one obligation to the next.

With the children gone, she could see from its absence what a weighted universe that had been, and also how full. But also how she and the girls had deceived him into believing that he was a part of that life, and not just a moon to her earth to their sun.

That duty was gone. Grown and departed. And the vibration of solitude barely hummed, and a new kind of fog had drawn in. An emptiness over morning coffee, a weariness when she dropped her robe outside the shower. And the magnet of this old, unspoken language—for better or for worse—began to tug again. It came from below, pulling her deeper into her seat.

He was driving. He had never driven. She supposed he had gone to the dealership and purchased this car all on his own, driven it all this time, brought it in for repairs, put gas in it, kept it clean. He had done all of that, and here she was, like a date, like a girl, sitting in his plush passenger seat without a word, while this unfamiliar man, this stranger, drove her to retrieve the children he had watched her birth.

Had they never parted, she knew for certain she would be driving. They would be speechless then, too, but with boredom and unspecified resentments. This new quiet was so fragile, so ripe, so suggestible that the mere breath of a word could displace it. Just past Toledo, June raised a hand, cleared her throat, and said, "Ferris wheel."

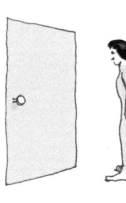
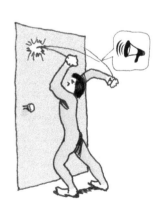

*photo by D. Kosiba*

Randall Jon Van Vynckt

# *Little Brother*

He'd once stood six-two in his uniform, proud, patriotic, bright-eyed and handsome as any twenty-year-old, but who was this here now, sitting hunched in the middle of the metal bed in the drab, antiseptic room, cowering under a blanket? Simply a victim of another war that shouldn't have happened, my older brother in the wrong place at the wrong time, driving over that IED in the sand.

I spoke softly to him, but not raising the cover, he yelled at me to go away, told me he didn't need pity, Mom and Dad's pity, my pity, the grandparents and aunts and uncles and cousins and his old friends, not even the dog, none of it.

Then the shaking started, heavy, because he had big shoulders, and the baritone sobs, and how I wanted to hold him, but he'd always been the one to save *me* from bullies, not the other way around, and I couldn't do it, just couldn't, just stood there in the doorway, hands in my pockets.

But it was a long drive home, hundreds of miles, and we needed to leave, so I stepped inside and picked up his duffel bag and waited some more, repeating his name, *Mikey, Mikey, time to go home*.

A few more minutes of silence, then the blanket slowly shrugged off, like the unveiling of a statue, and as he shifted himself toward the wheelchair at bedside, he looked right at me, and even with pleading, wet eyes, he was still my big brother, no longer six-two, but handsome as ever, so goddamned handsome.

Randall Jon Van Vynckt
## *The Stamp Collector*

Oh, aren't you just the dirtiest little boy on the block, sitting there in your shorts and t-shirt on the basement floor in your dad's hobby area leafing through the last five years' worth of his Popular Mechanics and making this kind of discovery? This is in the sixties, right, pre-digital, pre-photocopier even, when bulletins handed out in your sixth-grade class are mimeographed. Purple. And they smell funny.

Toward the front of every issue of Popular Mechanics are twenty pages chock full of classified ads. That's your holy grail, to heck with installing a flagstone patio on a budget, building a stereo bookcase, winterizing your outboard motor. And it would shock the neighbor boys and your two older brothers and dad and grandpa, too, but to heck even with the 1969 Chevy models previewed in the latest issue.

There are ads for Business Opportunities and Moneymaking Opportunities and Inventors Wanted, but you zero in on Stamp Collecting, which has dozens of ads, because this is long before Pac-Man, and if you're going to be non-athletic like you are and spend all your time indoors, stamp collecting is the most popular hobby in the world. The king of hobbies. Philately.

In fact, the queen of England collects stamps. On the back of your stamp album, there's a photo of Franklin Roosevelt enjoying his stamp collection. You're in good company.

All of you stamp collectors are philatelists, which is nothing to be ashamed of, but when one of the bullies is around on the playground, you drop that word like it's a dirty word: phi-lat-e-list. Now you know philately isn't a dirty word—you don't go to confession and tell the priest "Bless me, father. I have sinned, for I've collected stamps." He'd be quite disappointed. But bullies are dumb, and they know you're smart, which is one of the reasons they don't like you, that and because you wear glasses. And when they think you know something dirty that they don't, it drives them nuts.

Most of those classified ads in Popular Mechanics are three or four lines of the tiniest type and don't have pictures, but something is happening these days with the stamps of the Iron Curtain countries and a few emirates on the Persian Gulf, which no one has heard of because even the sheikhs who run them have only recently learned that they're sitting on a boat load of oil. Black gold… Texas tea, like they say on a favorite tv show, the Beverly Hillbillies.

These countries have decided to make a business of printing big, colorful postage stamps not to be used as postage, but for sale just to collectors. The oversized "topical" stamps feature cool subjects like dinosaurs and Olympic sports and space and early automobiles. And flowers and cats and dogs, and polka-dotted mushrooms like the ones your mom has on those plates hanging in the kitchen. And paintings.

That's what catches your eleven-year-old eye: an eighth-page display ad among the Stamp Collecting classifieds that offers "10 Nudes on Stamps for a Quarter." The picture shows the stamps, all of beautiful nude women—who cares if it's black and white? Rubens, Renoir, masters who knew their way around the female body. No Picassos, where you can't tell what the heck is going on.

Well, that was a morning well spent, leafing through dozens of magazines to find that one offer. Just adjust yourself a bit there when you stand up, head upstairs to find a quarter that you haven't spent on candy, and an envelope and stamp. Run, don't walk, to the mailbox.

It'll probably be a week before the naked ladies—wait, the topical art stamps—show up. In the meantime, just enjoy your dreams.

*photo by Carma Lynn Park*

Tim Chapman

## *The Metal Teeth of the Monster*

Sunday mornings we race the freights. Frank and Gerald and I are supposed to be in Sunday school, but we ditch a couple of times a month. Sometimes we go to the Walgreens to look at magazines, then we go down to the tracks and wait. The freights slow to a walk when they come into town. When they get to York Street they start to speed up again. That's where we start running. We run on the track bed, right next to the trains.

I'm running so fast that my suit coat is flapping against my back. I take off my tie and stuff it into my pocket. It's too tight anyway. I stay right next to the train for a while, then I start to cut loose. I love to pass the cars—flatbeds, tankers, boxcars. I run past an open boxcar. It's going so slow I could grab the ladder and swing myself up and ride it to Iowa or California or wherever it's going. For a second I imagine my mom, sitting alone at the dinner table, wondering where I am. Wondering if I'm dead or alive. Wondering if I'm at my dad's place in Santa Rosa. She has a plate of potatoes and corn, but she isn't eating. She just pushes it around with her fork and stares at the empty chair across the table.

I time my strides to the clacking of the huge wheels. The sun flashes off one as it turns. It'd slice you up good if you fell under it. I saw a movie once where a guy fell, and a train cut his leg off. You've got to be careful. I don't want to look around, but I do. Frank is right behind me, running hard, and Gerald, that stupid fuck, is wheezing along behind him. Gerald's face is red.

I met Frank and Gerald in Sunday school about a year ago. At first, I thought Gerald was shy because he didn't talk much. Then he started to say things. Every time I'd tell a joke he'd say, "Heard it!" right before the punch line, or if I'd mention that I liked some girl he'd grab his dick and make kissing noises. I wouldn't care, but Frank always laughs at his stupid cracks.

Sometimes Gerald doesn't want to race the freights, so we walk back to the church and hang out in the parking lot until the service lets out. He says he's worried that his parents are going to find out, but I think he's afraid of the trains.

The way we got started racing trains, we were talking about Heaven and Hell and the other stuff we had learned in Sunday school. I said if Heaven was so great why didn't we all just live there to begin with? Why even fool around with the earth? God could take us all up there whenever He wanted to, couldn't He?

I came up with the idea of racing the trains. I used to be afraid of them when I was a little kid. One time, Mom and I were sitting at a railroad crossing waiting for the train to pass. I must have looked nervous or something because she said, "Watch out! The monster is going to get you." Then she laughed.

Some day Frank and I are going to run ahead and jump across the tracks in front of the train. We haven't done it yet, though. We always chicken out at the last second.

I run next to the space between the cars, so I can look at the coupling. It looks like two right hands, gripping each other's fingers. The brake cable is swinging below it. The town flashes by through the gap. I turn and shout, "Let's go!" to Frank, and then I start to pour it on. Even with my church shoes on I can feel my toes grab the earth. The gravel crunches under my feet, and the dust feels sharp and hot in my nose. I'm so fast that grasshoppers are leaping to get out of my way, popping up just as I get to them. A sea of grasshoppers parts ahead of me. I hear Frank shout, "Come on Gerald, come on."

Frank lives across town, so on Saturday we ride our bikes and meet up somewhere, the mall or maybe down by the creek. Sometimes we throw a ball around, but usually we just talk. One Saturday we took some cheese and beef jerky and Cokes out to Graue Mill. It's this place where they have an old fashioned grinding stone for making flour that's powered by a water wheel in the creek. We waded across the dam next to the wheel and sat on this little island while we ate. I told Frank about the time I rode my bike back and forth in front of Gretchen Keller's house for an hour, hoping she'd come outside but also afraid she'd see me riding back and forth. He told me about the time his dad slapped his mom around, so he and his mom stayed at a motel for a few nights. I told Frank that I think Gerald is an idiot, and Frank said that he and Gerald have been friends since the third grade and I should shut up about him.

The engineer sees me as I pull even with him. He waves me away. I just grin. He shouts something, but the chugging of the engine and the sound of my blood pumping in my ears drowns him out. My heart sounds like it's going to pop, but I don't care; I feel great. The train is going faster now. I lean into it, and my thighs and calves are like iron bars, cutting through the air, pushing me forward. I'm up on my toes. My feet touch the ground just long enough. I'm out in front by three feet, then five feet, then ten feet. I cut left. I jump and time slows, and as I sail across the tracks I look at the horrible metal teeth of the monster. When my feet hit I throw myself forward and roll down the bank, into the weeds. As I get up I can see, flickering on and off between the cars, Frank and Gerald, standing on the other side.

*photo by D. Kosiba*

Carma Lynn Park

## *Crow Eats Carrion*

Crow's wife turns up her nose
and turns her back.  *You born in a barn*?
He brings her the wishbone of a wren.
*Here, sweetie, we'll make a wish*
*never to be parted*.

*Oh, you*.  She strokes the feathers
on top of his head.

When Crow eats carrion
he takes in that animal,
the light step of the deer,
the trembling of the rabbit,
the fish smoothed and smoothed by water.
He thinks he is god.
He stuffs himself.
His stomach hurts.  He has a headache.
*I'll never do this again*.

His wife has a cough that won't go away.
One morning she has blood on her beak.
One morning she doesn't wake,
though Crow calls and calls.
Now he knows for sure he's not god.

He eyes the sleek breast,
the muscle bunched in the thigh,
and knows what to do.
Bending his head
he begins to nibble on a wing.

Carma Lynn Park

## *A Coin for the Ferryman*

I think it is the end
but it opens.
I think it is my own blood
but it is a river of light.
I think it is a bird
but it is a boat.
I think it is a shadow
but it is the ferryman.

When I come to the landing
I explain that I left swiftly, without warning,
and did not bring a coin.
He says he will accept a poem.
So I stand at the bow
as the boat pulls away
and speak the truest words I know.

They might be drops of river spray;
they might be tears he wipes away.

*photo by Randall Jon Van Vynckt*

Crystal S. Rudds

## *Nothing But Dross*

It's hot in the office of Dr. What's His Name.
The wandering ivy on his desk sprawls like a wig thrown across the bed.
Her jewel-eyed daughter is there to help her listen with pad and pen,
but she feels alone.  The doctor and her daughter are children, after all, and her husband has
begun to regress.

Why had she left her good wig on the bed? This one sprawls over her eyes like the ivy's leaves. A
Wandering Jew, it was called.
She felt like a Jew, in the desert waiting on God,
alone with a white boy in a loose-shouldered coat delivering prophecies like an atheist.  With her
girl getting angry and her husband childlike, she felt old.  Pyramid-old. Dusty.
Is this how it would end, the nest emptied of both eggs and meaning?

She felt deserted, no sign from God, unmoored by the prophecy of leaving behind a home.
The doctor's mouth was moving, her daughter was scrawling notes--
So this was how it ended. Eggs emptied and a nest's unraveled meaning--
and between their words (the alphabet her husband had lost),
Mrs. N-- found life reduced.

Crystal S. Rudds

## *Losing Your Change*

I hate a woman
who walks with an open purse,

zipper split to creation.
That careless illusion of

the carefree, as if wolves
don't maraud grocery

parking lots looking for easy meat, as if
her pearls are plenty to come by

or lint in the seams of a person's life
isn't worth the pinching.

She must not know what's in there.
Those pennies greened from want

of a slower world need the dark. Take
myself: what if I had never had the time

to cultivate my charge? These poems,
black seeds, black dirt, waiting for water

and light. You have to protect the small
space there is to force a change.

I saw a woman on Cottage Grove once, leopard fur
coat bald as a used spare tire.  Doesn't

anyone care these days? Doesn't anyone
recognize the weight of a pocketbook?


To bear the strap across one's shoulder,

to clutch your gold to the chest,

only to be undone by some mental trifle
is cosmically unjust. Why, the threat alone could

leave a woman clueless,

spinning around in the middle of the El train, yelling
at ghosts, losing all of her change.

And who knows, who knows what lethal thing might fall from her bag--
whether gun or diamond or thought?

Crystal S. Rudds

## *The Hook*

Glad I'm not in love with you.
Said, glad I'm not in love with you.
Glad the sight of your frame
In the door, long
Like the neck of my favorite beer
Don't slay me, flay me—
Baby, I'm glad you're gone.

Watch me shimmy to the jukebox:
    Hooking,
        Cooking,
     Juking

All alone.  Glaad
I'm not in love.
Gave you even the lint in my pockets,
And your absence
Has done left me short-changed, sense
Just about gone.

Crystal S. Rudds

## *Marital Pests*

We should have got them upon arrival
When they marched into the living room,
Sentried, a hundred black pearls in a line.
They were ordered then,
Easy to keep track. We weren't infiltrated.

We should have got the broom,
Emptied the flasks of youth on the kitchen floor and
Whomped them,
Made wine from misery.  Instead,
We watched.

The balding eyelashes that were legs
Entertained us at first,
Our own little Pheidole circus.
But how colonies multiply,
                            left unhampered.

Soon, we were pinching
Them for sport to get to the bottom of something,
Anything.  Black blood
Dead incense of spring
Trap Jaw
Lasius
Under sugar.


We let them go too long.

And now,
They're crawling all over the table at Behrins, Behrins, & Wallack.

Fucking ants.

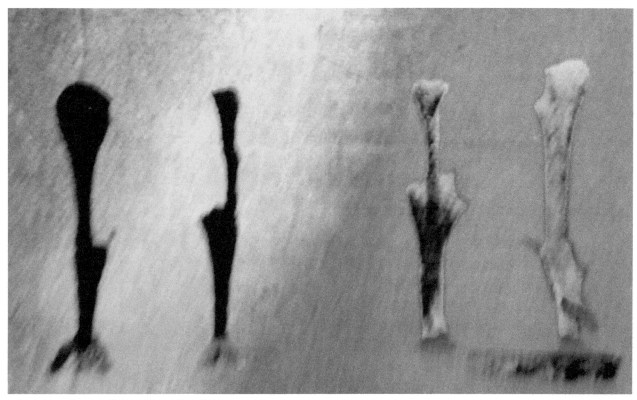

*photo by Randall Jon Van Vynckt*

Lani Montreal

# *Foam*

It is only when trying to buy a sofa
that you find out there's a crisis of foam
The fancy furniture store guy tells you
like you should know about it

Well, you know there's the issue with foam right?
You know, memory foam... It used to be we can deliver
4-6 weeks, but now it's 24 weeks, maybe more!
Hmmm, really? I say, as I run fingers over the velvet chaise,
walk around an ottoman to try out a sectional
press down the cushion to check for firmness

Well, there's Covid and what happened to Texas, all those
chemicals needed for production—you know—
propylene oxide, glycerine... (Sounds like a recipe
from the anarchist cookbook) then, that boat
that got hijacked... (hah, how inconvenient)
My mind flies by this time because really
all I want is a fucking daybed, but you don't
realize how connected things are...the big freeze
in Texas the storm in Louisiana the fires
in California the war in Iran the red tagging
in the Philippines the dead in India
rising
rising
rising
like a tsunami waiting to happen in Japan.

Lani Montreal

## *Things to Remember from This Trip Back Home*

You never bring enough clothes to the beach
It matters to look nice even in this heat, where
You sweat, stink, take more showers, sweat
Here, flavors explode without apology
Coffee is strong when brewed,
But not when in packets of 3-in-1
Dessert is too sweet, too plenty
Don't be scared that someone in your family will go into a diabetic shock
Their blood is a quarter sugar
Your teeth will crumble into salt after eating something savory
You'll keep tasting patis long after you've left

Don't forget that here, people love hard
They are always teenagers in search of a high
Love is best when illicit
Lechon, when de leche
The sun sears your skin till it's crispy
The rains will give you pulmunya
Mosquitoes will fuck you over
As if you did them wrong in a previous life
They'll make your nose bleed, your blood platelet count low

You will blow through your money like rain falling though broken roof
It is cheap, so cheap, you can get three massages in a week
Treat everybody to a movie
Buy things you will never use
Pasalubongs for people who didn't even know you left
Lives too are cheap, so cheap
People are shot for smoking weed; children, from sniffing glue
Ah, just collateral damage

Politicians have billboards the size of a building
No choice but to stare at them when stuck in traffic
And at skin-whitening products peddled by mestizas

You will be stuck in traffic, more than once; in fact, more often than not
So don't forget to be patient, or maybe rent a personal hotspot, make sure
You're never without WiFi; always connected

Some days, though, the road is clear, not congested
Time matters, is not wasted waiting or looking at billboards
Or at crowds of passengers stranded at bus stops,
Waiting for a ride home past midnight

Remember, remember, because the gap steals your memory
You don't recall the bumpy ride on the jeepney at 2AM
Elbows that crept against your exposed skin
How men molested you with their sleepy heads
Their restless arms
Their open legs

Don't forget you left your summer clothes behind,
Languishing in your sister's closet 'til your next visit
Your mother won't be giving them away to disaster victims

She's not there anymore.

Don't be wondering when summer in Chicago comes
And you can't find your blue dress
Remember you live in the in-between
Nothing is ever really lost.

Lani Montreal

# *If I Die Tomorrow*

Please make a fucking fuss
I traveled halfway around the world to be something
You will not not cry as if my dying means nothing
Once I thought I was
Nothing
I thought I could disappear
and no one would even know or care
I liked disappearing
I made a career out of running away
when I first discovered the power of flight

If I die tomorrow I hope it will be easy
I denounce difficulty
Hard work is too hard
Yet I did wash dishes 10 hours a day
I did walk in below-zero temperature to get to work
Clutching my lungs as if they were going to fall out
I did wait tables and dealt with messy eaters
Filled up empty condiment bottles with ketchup, soy sauce and vinegar
Smiled until my face hurt for an extra dollar tip
I did take care of children who colored their sky pink and their monsters purple

When first I crossed the border and my savings ran out
I wanted to go back home
There, where people thought I could be something
I wanted to stay a teenager on my friend's porch
Drink gin and seven up at dusk
Play mahjong all night
Smoke stolen marlboros until my lungs hurt and my throat, torn to shreds
Pray I do not wake choking in puke and blood-tainted phlegm

Sometimes the things that keep us alive are the things that kill us
Remember the white guy in Kung Fu found dead in a closet?
Amy Winehouse, Whitney Houston?
The water was still warm in the tub when they found her

bop

And what about that pretty young thing
who inched her way to the brink to catch that perfect selfie?
Did she even get to post it?
Took 6 hours to pick her off the landing.

If I die tomorrow, sure, say some prayers, although I prefer poetry
Toasts and tales and yes, a little karaoke
My dog would lie on my side of the bed waiting for me to pet her
I know at least my daughter would cry
She always cried when sending me off at the airport
I know my husband would tell jokes
And my son would smoke weed all day and hide his grief in the fog.

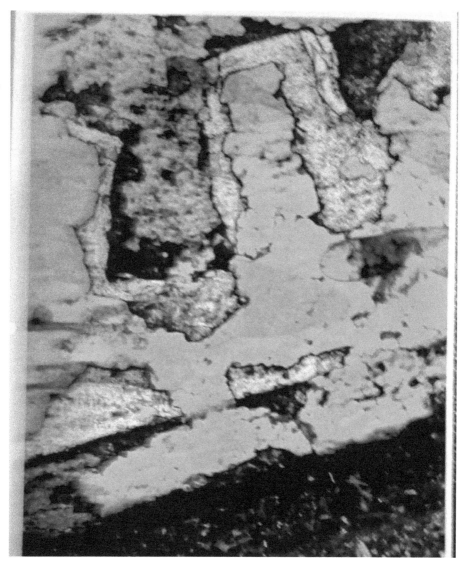

*photo by Randall Jon Van Vynckt*

Rachel L. Robbins

## *The Mathematician's Wife*

### A Theorem (Woman)

Arithmetic drifted in her clouds. Newton chiseled worry lines into her face, literature knitted her hair, tangles of physics brushed freckled shoulders. Her eyes, absolute zero. Green. A matrix. I held her hand.

She unraveled, thread by silvery thread. Atoms eroded from fingertips, exponents wallowed in shadow. The residue of her numbers hovered, investigating pretzel crumbs long forgotten.

### A Hyperbola (Clock)

She made apples fall from trees. She shook Darwin's sun. Fractions and exponents multiplied in crushed footprints, forgotten. I calculated her. Strange 7s perched in trees, 8s multiplied in the breeze; I knew, the way you know about a melon.

I thought X would remain constant. I forgot to factor Y (Years) and Z (memory).

### A Ratio (Spiderweb)

The mathematics of daffodils. Her sun hat to sundress; 3:1. Atoms still picked over pretzel crumbs. I longed for the proper equation to explain her back into the ivy.

X got forgetful. Forgot to take her medicine, forgot to take her bath, forgot to wear her bra at the grocery. X even forgot Y.

### Symmetry (Evening)

Daffodils. Just me and the ivy, blowing and growing, unraveling into entropy in a garden.

Rachel L. Robbins

## *Tales from My Fisherman Father*

In Tiburon on a Wednesday, I saw a seabird with my father's face.
Why don't you get yourself a decent boyfriend? It cawed
It spiraled up and vanished, casting a flicker on the sand by my feet, like the limb of a tree
breathing out slowly.

*

That night, I dreamt that my father was eaten by a bear. It swallowed him whole, like a shot of
Slivovitz, and expressed disgust at the aftertaste. The bear's belly bulged, and his chin sprouted a
long, tangled beard. When the bear began to hoard flashlights and parked himself in front of old
Star Wars reruns on the Sci-Fi Channel, I grew suspicious. When the bear began to snore with all
the rhythm and force of the ocean, I realized there was salvation in hibernation.

*

When I turned seven, my father's beard filled with salmon and seaweed. His cod eyes darted from
reef to reef. He spoke in an enormous gurgling noise which made everything sound underwater.

This was his lullaby. It was the sort of burbling tonality I needed in order to believe in things like
that stuff that shifts the clouds.

*

When my father was a child, a shark bit off his arm. He replaced it with a wooden stump.

Naturally, he became a shark hunter, and he hated all trees for daring to resemble him. Stumps
were the worst of the trees, because they were already dead.

*

My father was tormented by winter fish. He saw them everywhere: dangling from the trees,
hanging in the air like reflective lures, swallowing the sky and hiccupping green ocean. I tried to
explain to him that they were only apples. See, they're not fish at all, I said as I plucked a red, ripe
one, but his scaly skin tautened, and so, like he had taught me so many times, I threw it back. I
watched it fall like an unanswered plea until at last, the apple hit the ocean.

*

My skeleton is shivering, he said to me once, when his thoughts turned to winter.

*

One Passover, I brought home a handsome, rich, fish of a boyfriend.
Is he Jewish? asked my father, clutching the neighborhood in the palm of his hand.

*

Once, in the hospital, my father ate an octopus. As he chomped, his eyes rolled back like a hungry
predator. I watched all the legs and legs and legs. I remember he had looked like an octopus, all

those tubes growing from his arms. I had never felt my fingers so concretely, so many unnecessary digits. That was when I first noticed it, supple and strange, a perfect tentacle sprouting from the heart of my palm.

If you follow your hands, you can shake the winter fish from the trees, he said.

*

There we stood, just two humans looking out the hospital window, at the edges of the fish bowl, talking about the weather.

*

My father's stump arm flailed wildly as the train shook. When we went underground, my father got confused.  Look, he insisted, There's a beautiful glowing fish at the end of the tunnel.

*

We'll call him Charlie, my father said once of a tremendous rainbow trout, as he gutted it and the paint colors spilled out. The clouds were gray as fish skin. My father wiped the purple blood on his pants and said, Don't worry, Sweets.  He's already dead.

*

I knew when the clocks were still in the fish skin sky, and the carp rained down from the dying trees like ripe apples.  Be still, said my father, fishing for forbidden fruit. The leaves hummed, and everywhere were tentacles for hearts. I knew then that this was the beginning of something slow.

Rachel L. Robbins

## *Ode to Aimee Bender*

When I was a child it became clear to me that my father was different from other fathers. He was gruff and unkempt, and told strange stories about the sea. He wasn't that old, but his hair was white, and his wrinkles left deep impressions in his skin, like footprints in wet sand. His eyes were two boats casting towards the horizon.

Twenty years have passed, and it's clear now that I am losing him. My father is returning to the ocean, slowly, in the same way that we all eventually return to dust. He scratches at his beard that flaps with minnows, and when he stands in the light I can see purple and red tadpoles swimming through his veins.

When I realized my father was growing fins and gills, I wasn't upset at first. I wanted to get to know this new marine father, to understand, and smell, and swim with him, but I didn't realize my father wasn't coming back.

He told me he never meant to lose himself at sea. He just loved the chase and the storm.  We're long-lining through the cold front, he would say, holding his red thumb to the wind like a flagpole to the moon.  It's about alkalinity, he said, brushing algae from his anchor, and I'm angling for stragglers.  This had something to do with his method: isolating the weak from the pack.

I did the math. A few weeks ago, he complained his heart felt heavy as a fish on the line. Last Saturday he said his tongue was slimy and thick, like an eel. At this rate, I figure we have about a month left. I took him shopping, tried to dress him up more like a man and less like an Arctic salmon. The clothes kept snagging on hooks and doorknobs. I'm cooked bait, he said, and there were marlins diving and breaching in the fog between us.

Yesterday, I found him flopping in his favorite chair, restless like a carp out of water. I looked into his round, glassy eyes and fed him bits of algae and plankton. But he's shrinking. Anyone can see. This morning he was a minnow. I didn't want to come home one day to find him minuscule, molecular, floating in a coffee cup above the mantle like whale food. I had to set him free.

So I drove to the coast, with my father, the minnow, in a fish bowl strapped into the passenger seat, frolicking as the water sloshed from side to side. From his erratic swimming I could tell he was nervous about the imminent storm, and my driving on slick roads.  It's okay, Dad, I said, patting the fish bowl as though it were his hand. He kept worrying about what to cook for dinner, and whether I would ever marry that boyfriend. I held my finger to my lips to shush his worried flapping, and he stopped circling the bowl, and I realized we both knew we were headed somewhere strange.

I poured him lovingly into the ocean and watched the water blend and stir. I stood there hoping he would swim away into the depths; I waited until the sky began to darken and the ocean became the air became the ocean. Still, when I am near the water, I hear my father whispering. Sweets, he croons, The whole world is a fishbowl.

I pace the edges of the ocean, forlorn, squinting at the walls of the sky. I keep my door unlocked. I keep my lights on. I know he isn't coming back, but if he does, I want him to find his way. When the fog sits on the house in the morning, I cry out for him and hope he'll hear. But I know he can't hear me underwater. I know that to him my voice is muted by the ocean, and all he can hear are sea shanties sinking towards the bottom.

Rachel L. Robbins

## *Two Wrongs*

She asked him to invent her a color.  Without missing a beat, he said, "Malarkia—
It's a mix between orange and red, and it glows in the dark.  It stimulates your heart rate and helps planes land in the dark.  It's the color of plums right before they ripen.  It feels furry to touch, like peaches, and if you peel back its layers, it gets softer still, like velvet."

"Malarkia can make people fall in love," he continued, eyeing a stranger across the room.  "It's like looking through glass windows at the ocean, an oversized fish tank.  It's a dangerously emotive color spectrum.  Malarkia-colored fish feed on smaller malarkia-colored fish in the sea.  And when they knew to look for them, the cardiologists saw them in their microscopes—malarkia-colored fish swimming in our veins, laying malarkia eggs in our poor malarkia hearts."

"Because the world is perfect," he said.  "Stars are perfect.  The wind is perfect.  But people are not perfect.  People fall in love with the wrong people.  And when they die, having loved someone with every ounce of their strangely colored hearts, they wish there was a word for the color they feel filling them up, ripening."

*photo by Randall Jon Van Vynckt*

Rob Sokolick

## *Our Feet Beneath Us*

Our feet have grown with us
They remember all that we've done
and everywhere we've gone

They are the recorders of our bodies our minds our spirits
When cold water splashes on them it sends an awakening ring up the legs and spine
like that carnival game in which a hammer blow fires a weight skyward to
(hopefully)
ring a bell

They remind our joints
after a long hike
not to be so hard on them

They reward us with a pillowy feeling
(looking for something less laborious than walking on clouds)
when we slide them into a new pair of shoes and socks

They disappear beneath us like a unicorn when we run and then reappear
as if to say the unicorn was there all along

It's difficult to comprehend how such a small part of us,
with ten toes performing in unison like the coupling rods
that connect the wheels on a locomotive,
can perform such a considerable undertaking

And when we ultimately reach our climax in this sphere of mysteries and fascinations
our feet will carry us on to our next quest
and begin recording again

*photo by Randall Jon Van Vynckt*

# Contributors

**Carma Lynn Park** is a Chicago-based writer and photographer who began writing poems and taking photos at an early age and couldn't be stopped. Her poems have appeared in such publications as *3LIGHTS, American Goat, Beauty / Truth, Dark Regions, Hammers, Mythic Delirium, Prune Juice, Red Shoes Review, Talebones*, and *Tales of the Talisman*. She wants to thank her writing group for their advice and support.

**Christine Sneed** is the author of four books, most recently the novel Paris, He Said and the story collection The Virginity of Famous Men. Her work has appeared in The Best American Short Stories, O. Henry Prize Stories, Ploughshares, New England Review, New York Times, and other publications. She has received the Grace Paley Prize, the Chicago Writers' Association Book of the Year Award, the Chicago Public Library Foundation's 21st Century Award, among other honors, and has been a finalist for the Los Angeles Times Book Prize. She teaches for Northwestern University's School of Professional Studies' MFA program and for the low-residency MFA program at Regis University. She lives in Pasadena, California.

**Crystal S. Rudds** holds an MFA from Indiana University-Bloomington and a PhD from the University of Illinois. Her creative work has appeared in *Obsidian, NightBallet Press, Root Work Journal* and been nominated for an Illinois Arts Council Literary Award. She is currently an assistant professor of literature at The University of Utah in Salt Lake City.

**D. Kosiba** was born at very young age in Poland that was at the time under communist regime. As soon as she was able to locate USA on the map - she started to dream about going there. After learning a completely wrong language - German and graduating from Jagiellonian University in Cracow, she relocated to Chicago where she currently resides. She enjoys organizing live music events (activity currently a bit on a hiatus), making dark chocolate truffles and photographing random things around her.

**Jennifer Worrell** got hooked on writing stories in kindergarten using mimeographed prompts. Her supplier, Mrs. Davenport, kept a stash of the Purple Monster handy for a quick fix. Though she kicked the habit for a short time, Jenny's writing problem has spiraled out of control. But don't worry. She can quit whenever she wants to.

Her debut novel, *Edge of Sundown*, was published by Darkstroke Books in November 2020. She also is proud to be featured in several literary journals, such as Writing Disorder, Write City Magazine, Raconteur, and Little Old Lady Comedy. You can visit her on her website at www. jenniferworrelwrites.com or FB/Twitter/Instygram @JWorrellWrites, where she'd be glad to discuss anything from books and music to the merits of single vs. double-crust pie.

**Katherine Ace** was born in Chicago in 1953, and fell in love with oil paint at the age of 10 at a summer children's class at the Art Institute of Chicago. She began painting in oils regularly at the age of 14, and through high school had a small space in the basement of her home where she painted several hours a day. Ace went on to study art at Knox College in Galesburg, Illinois, graduating in 1975. After college Ace had a series of art-related jobs started in New Orleans, Vermont and Boston and then moved west – copying Old Masters paintings, working as a potter, doing graphics work and serving as a quick sketch artist in New Orleans and casinos in Reno, NV and Lake Tahoe, CA. She worked extensively on illustrations for text books producing a series of 16 books for Rorke Publishing and 36 portraits of composers for Simon and Shuster's World of Music. In January 1990 Ace moved to Portland, Oregon where she has lived ever since, focusing on her own poetic paintings, which have been shown extensively across the country. Ace has always worked in her home, be it in garages, basement, kitchen, 8'x10' bedroom in a double wide mobile home which she lived in also. In 1999 she added onto her shop/garage to make a large, light and truly functional studio.

**L.C. Fiore's** new novel is *Coyote Loop* (Adelaide Books, 2021). His historical novel *The Last Great American Magic* won Novel of the Year from Underground Book Reviews. His debut novel, *Green Gospel*, was named First Runner-Up in the Eric Hoffer Book Awards. His writing has appeared in Ploughshares, Michigan Quarterly Review, and many others, as well as in various baseball publications, including The Love of the Game: Essays by Lifelong Fans (McFarland & Co.). He is the communications director for the North Carolina Writers' Network and lives in Chapel Hill, NC, with his family: www.lcfiore.com.

**Lani T. Montreal** is a queer Filipina writer and educator. Her works have been published and produced in the Philippines, Canada, the U.S. and in Cyberspace. She teaches writing at Malcolm X College and lives and loves in Albany Park, Chicago with her multicultural and multi-species family. Her blog (updated sporadically) filinthegap.com

**Libby Fischer Hellmann** left a career in broadcast news in Washington, DC and moved to Chicago a long time ago, where she, naturally, began to write gritty crime fiction. She soon began writing historical fiction as well. Sixteen novels and twenty-five short stories later, she claims they'll take her out of the Windy City feet first. She has been nominated for many awards in the mystery and crime writing community and has even won a few. She has been a finalist twice for the Anthony and four times for Foreword Magazine's Book of the Year. She has also been nominated for the Agatha, the Shamus, the Daphne, and has won the IPPY, Foreword Magazine's Indie Awards, and the Readers Choice Award multiple times. Her novels include the newly-released historical novel, *A BEND IN THE RIVER*, set mostly in Vietnam during the war. She has also written the five-volume Ellie Foreman series, which she describes as a cross between "Desperate Housewives" and "24;" the hard-boiled 5-volume Georgia Davis PI series, and four other stand-alone historical thrillers set during Revolutionary Iran, Cuba, the Sixties, and WW2. Her short stories have been published in a dozen anthologies, the Saturday Evening Post, and Ed Gorman's "25 Criminally Good Short Stories" collection. Her books have been translated into Spanish, German, Italian, and Chinese. All her books are available in print, ebook, and audiobook. Libby also hosts Second Sunday Books, a monthly podcast where she interviews bestselling and emerging authors. In 2006 she was the National President of Sisters in Crime, a 4000 member organization committed to the advancement of female crime fiction authors.

**Molia Dumbleton's** fiction has appeared in Best Small Fictions, Kenyon Review, New England Review, Cincinnati Review, SmokeLong Quarterly, Witness, and elsewhere. Her work has been awarded the Seán Ó Faoláin Story Prize and Columbia Journal Winter Award, and her debut collection of stories was a finalist for the Iowa Short Fiction Award. She is currently an Assistant Fiction Editor for Split Lip Magazine and a member of the Curatorial Board at Ragdale, and was invited to serve as a reader for the 2021 AWP Grace Paley Prize for Short Fiction and AWP Series Prize for the Novel. She has a B.A. from Oberlin College, an M.A. from Rice University, an M.A. in Creative Writing from Northwestern University, and an M.F.A. in Writing from Bennington College. She teaches Creative Writing at DePaul University.

**Rachel L. Robbins** received her MFA from the School of the Art Institute of Chicago in 2010. She is a tenured assistant professor at Malcolm X College and adjunct faculty at the School of the Art Institute of Chicago. She is a commissioned muralist for Chicago's 35th, 39th, 46th and 47th wards. Rachel recently completed sculpture installations on Michigan Avenue as a donation to PAWS Chicago, two of which have been placed on permanent display at the University of Wisconsin, Madison. Her work has appeared in *Thrice Fiction*, Driftwood Press, The Kenyon Review, Rattle Poetry, and The Brooklyn Rail among others. Rachel won Rhino Poetry's Founder's Prize and was nominated by Rhino Poetry for the Pushcart Prize in 2015. She was nominated by Make Literary Magazine for the Pushcart Prize in 2018. Rachel won the Illinois Arts Council Agency Literary Award in 2019 for an excerpt from her forthcoming historical fiction novel, Enola Spelled Backward. She is the author of *In Lieu of Flowers*, available through Tortoise Books.
To see the full scope of her work, please refer to her website: www.rachelslotnick.com.

**Randall Jon Van Vynckt** has contributed short stories to four e-anthologies from Write Volumes: *Shades of Horror and Strangeness*, 2019; *Shades of Transition & Transformation*,

2020; *Shades of Chicago*, 2021; and *Shades of Positively Pandemic*, 2021. His writing includes flash fiction, short stories, essays, memoirs, and novellas, and he's a dozen years into a novel. In a past life, he published essays about historic places, edited an architectural dictionary, and wrote erotic fan fiction. His photos capture unexpected beauty in the aging built environment.

**Rob Sokolick** was a chemist, a trapeze artist, and a good friend. He succumbed to injuries he received pursuing his many loves. Requiescat in pace June 3, 1968 - June 2, 2021.

**Sara Peak Convery** was born and raised in Iowa. Her creativity was mostly expressed through sewing, until college when she began to paint. Her early artworks were often personal: family history through direct observation. After moving to Chicago, she shifted to video, working as a wedding videographer and editor. After the death of her father, in 2005, Convery revisited the college artwork stashed in her parents' attic and decided to return to painting. Completed in 2013, "I Never Said I Wasn't Happy," a documentary about her parents' marriage, brought together 25 years of interviews, artwork, and archival material. In 2014, Convery decided to show her artwork publicly. Her first successes were in small cooperative galleries in northwest Indiana. The 2016 election triggered a shift in her work to political concerns. She began reconstructing US flags to show the distressed state of the country. In early 2017 she was diagnosed with cancer and created a series of works again relating to personal experience but more universally relatable. In 2018 Convery moved her studio into a storefront. She established Slacks Window Gallery in 2019. Convery maintains an active art practice and enjoys curating exhibitions and collaborating with other artists.

**Tim Chapman** is a former forensic scientist for the Chicago Police Department and writing instructor at Malcolm X College. He holds a Master's degree in Creative Writing from Northwestern University. His fiction has been published in The Southeast Review, the Chicago Reader, Alfred Hitchcock's Mystery Magazine, Palooka, and the anthology, *The Rich and the Dead*. His first novel, *Bright and Yellow, Hard and Cold*, (re-released as *A Trace of Gold*) was a finalist in Shelf Unbound's 2013 Best Indie Book competition. His short stories have been collected under the title *Kiddieland and other misfortunes*. His latest novel is *The Blue Silence*. When he's not writing he's teaching martial arts or painting pretty pictures.
Visit him at www.thrillingtales.com, (Facebook) FB.com/realTimChapman,
(Twitter) @realTimChapman, (Instagram) @realTimChapman.

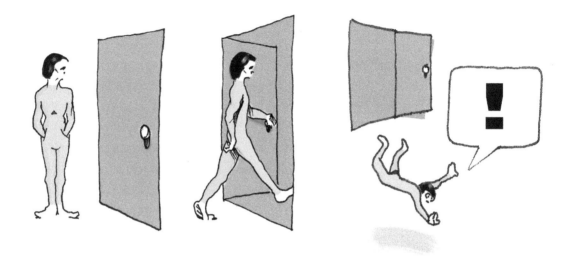

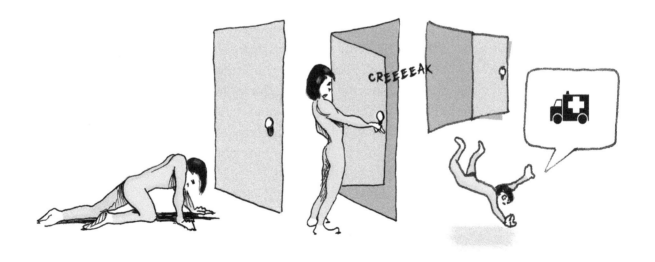

## *Publication History*

"In Limbo" first appeared in The Ottawa Object (2015)

"The Monkey's Uncle Louis" first appeared in New England Review, Vol. 39, No. 3, 2018, and received a Special Mention in the *Pushcart Prize XLIV* anthology.

"Your Sweet Man" first appeared in *Chicago Blues: A Collection of Crime Stories About the Real Windy City*. Bleak House Books, 2007

"Secret Garden" and "The Metal Teeth of the Monster" first appeared in the anthology *Kiddieland and other misfortunes* 2017

"Cross Your Fingers" was a finalist in the 2017 Iron Writer Challenge

"A Coin for the Ferryman" first appeared in Tales of the Talisman Volume IV, Issue 3, December 2008

"Crow Eats Carrion" first appeared in Mythic Delirium No. 13, Summer / Fall 2005

CPSIA information can be obtained
at www.ICGtesting.com
Printed in the USA
BVHW021949290921
617774BV00009B/255